THE ELECTRICAL GENIUS OF LIBERTY HALL

CHARLES PROTEUS STEINMETZ

(1865–1923)

". . . *Spiritual power is a force which history clearly teaches has been the greatest force in the development of men.*"
—*Charles Proteus Steinmetz*

CHARLES PROTEUS STEINMETZ
Portrait courtesy of *The Reader's Digest*

THE ELECTRICAL GENIUS OF LIBERTY HALL

CHARLES PROTEUS STEINMETZ

BY FLOYD MILLER

FOREWORD BY CLYDE WAGONER

Illustrated with Photographs

McGRAW-HILL BOOK COMPANY, INC.

NEW YORK TORONTO LONDON

ACKNOWLEDGMENTS

No man writes a book alone; what he puts on paper is often interesting or accurate to the degree that others have helped him. Certainly, the General Electric Corporation has been of greatest assistance, opening their files and laboratories to my research. Emil Remscheid, once a Steinmetz lab boy, re-created for me that fateful day when lightning struck Camp Mohawk. Clyde Wagoner, who contributes a foreword to this book, guided me in many important ways. John Anderson Miller, whose own work on Steinmetz was published by the American Society of Mechanical Engineers, was more than generous of his time and his material. But without Steinmetz's grandchildren, Joe Hayden and Marjory Hayden, this book could not have seen print. They opened their hearts and their memories to me. In a very real sense this book is more theirs than mine, for they lived it.

THE ELECTRICAL GENIUS OF LIBERTY HALL

Library of Congress Catalog Card Number: 62-19159

All of the photographs, unless otherwise credited, are from the Hayden Family Photograph Album.

For Meg, whose extraordinary combination of talents has sustained the author and would have delighted the hero of this book

FOREWORD

The life of Charles Proteus Steinmetz was a *true* Horatio Alger story. He was born a frail hunchback to parents in the most meager of circumstances. His mother died while he was still a child and he had to face life without the love and protection he so badly needed. Yet, against these odds, he became a great scientist, a benefactor of mankind, and he was revered and honored throughout the world.

My first contact with this electrical genius was back in 1915 when I was a reporter on a Schenectady newspaper. There was considerable public interest in the problem of the country's diminishing coal supply and my editor suggested that I interview Steinmetz on the question. Steinmetz was working for General Electric, living in Schenectady, and had already made a great reputation. I had seen this man riding his bicycle to and from work and heard stories of his extraordinary mind, but I had never met him. All of us in town were a bit in awe of him, and no other newspaper man had had the temerity to seek an interview. So it was with some misgiving that I rang his doorbell that night.

He greeted me with a very pleasant "Hello" and invited me into his house. At the same time his piercing eyes scanned me, measured me, and I feared that at any moment he would announce that my problem was much too insignificant for him to bother with and that I would be dismissed. But the contrary happened. He kneeled on a chair, rested his arms on its back, and prepared to give me all the time and information I required. He talked of the country's vast undeveloped water power, calling it "white coal," and predicted that the time would come when it would supply enough energy to light all the homes and factories of the nation.

We talked for an hour and he made wonderful copy, for he had the ability to explain a highly technical problem in simple and understandable words. I came away with an exclusive story that brought me much praise from my editor, all because of a great man's kindness and consideration to an unknown reporter. That interview also marked the beginning of a close friendship that continued until Steinmetz's death in 1923.

I became a publicist for General Electric during the years when Steinmetz was the company's chief consulting engineer, and I learned firsthand that he was not the strange recluse that much of the public believed him to be. He loved people and enjoyed his association with them. My frequent visits to his home and his summer camp on the Mohawk River were warm and memorable. No matter how busy he might be, he always had time for a chat and for the examination of my ideas and problems.

Steinmetz was an idealist and dedicated his life to the betterment of man's lot in the world. His contributions to electricity were important and many but not his only concern. He was active in civic affairs, in conservation, in education. Above all, he loved children. He was never happier than when in their company. Knowing Steinmetz enriched my life. Reading about him can enrich yours. He was a genius, but also a warm and lovable man.

—Clyde D. Wagoner

CHAPTER ONE

THE POLICE DESK sergeant answered the phone in a weary voice. He was long past being surprised by any folly man could devise. He listened to a flood of excited words, then said, "Madam, there are no alligators in Schenectady."

Again came the torrent of words and he held the receiver slightly away from his ear to ease the impact. "In the Erie Canal!" he finally exclaimed. "Now, how would alligators get into the Erie Canal? You probably saw some floating logs." He rolled his eyes heavenward, apparently seeking some source of patience beyond his own. Finally, picking up a pencil, he said, "All right, Madam, all right. We'll investigate. Now, just where in the canal did you see them? At Liberty and College streets? I'll send some men."

After he hung up he stared a moment at his notes, then turned to a lieutenant standing nearby. "Liberty and College streets—isn't that where that nut Steinmetz lives?"

"That *genius* Steinmetz lives," the lieutenant corrected gently.

"Nut ... genius! There's a difference? The point is, I've heard he has some weird animals for pets. Suppose some of them escaped?   There may really be alligators in the Erie Canal!"

When the police arrived at Liberty Street they found the entire neighborhood had turned out to lean over the bridge that spanned the Erie Canal and connected the old downtown section of the city with the newer uptown part.   In the normally placid canal water there were occasional turbulences and flashes of scaly bodies; along one shore there floated a rough snout and a pair of protuberant eyes that stared with stony interest at the human beings on the bridge above.   Undeniably, these were alligators.

Information and advice came to the police from all sides.   The alligators belonged to Steinmetz, all right, and the neighborhood had long been apprehensive about just such an escape as this.   One woman, pointing to the large, brick Victorian house with heavily bracketed eaves and a series of bay windows, exclaimed, "Strange things go on in that Steinmetz house."

"What sort of things?" the sergeant asked.

"Well, he lives with animals, and believe me, these alligators aren't the worst by any means.   And at night strange noises come out of that house, and weird lights appear in the windows.   They say he's an inventor, but what I want to know is what's he inventing?   He's a foreigner and maybe it's something that will blow us all up."

"I don't know anything about that," the sergeant said. "Our job right now is to get these alligators out of the canal."

Poles and nets were produced and a half-dozen policemen now began the hazardous job of urging the stubborn alligators into captivity. After some minutes of intense and fruitless activity a stir suddenly went through the crowd of spectators and word was passed: "Steinmetz is coming." The south side of the canal was lined with warehouses and in front of them was Dock Street, which led a mile away to the gaunt and gloomy buildings of the General Electric Company where Charles Steinmetz was employed.

Now approaching up Dock Street was a small ball of a man hunched over the handlebars of a bicycle, pedaling hard. The crowd parted for him and he dropped to the ground in front of the policemen with the nets. He was a familiar sight in the neighborhood, having moved into the large house the year before, 1897; even so, his appearance remained something of a shock. When he climbed from the bicycle and stood erect he was less than five feet tall and was cruelly deformed. His spindly legs supported a thick torso with a hump that protruded high on his right shoulder; his overlarge head was covered with disheveled hair and his face with a bristly beard. His appearance was sometimes a little disturbing to small children. They were too young to see the gentleness and the pain in his blue eyes behind the thick pince-nez glasses.

Steinmetz leaned over the bridge railing and looked at his alligators. He shook his head, partly to himself and partly to the policeman beside him, and murmured, "Ach, they wanted a swim. The wind must have carried the smell of the canal water to them and so they do what is in their nature to do."

"Well, they sure can't swim in the Erie Canal," the sergeant exclaimed.

Steinmetz smiled. "No, I do not suppose that would be considered proper. If you will catch them in your net I will take them home and make certain they do not swim again. But please do not hurt them."

"*Me* hurt *them!* Mister, that's not the problem."

After considerable maneuvering one of the alligators was netted and lifted from the water. It came up snorting and thrashing; the crowd of spectators gasped and retreated from the bridge. Several policemen unholstered their guns. Steinmetz darted forward to lift the beast out of the netting and cradle it in his arms. He murmured soothingly, rubbed its belly, and immediately the thrashing ceased. Whether or not an alligator's leathery face can assume an expression is certainly debatable, but there were those in the crowd who claimed to see a beatific smile. In any event, the animal made no further struggles and allowed its master to return it to the outdoor pen beside the big Victorian house. As the crowd parted to allow the two to pass, there were some whispered and cruel jokes about the matching ugliness of man and beast.

Seven alligators were removed from the canal and tenderly returned to their pen by Steinmetz. When the last transfer was completed, the sergeant said, "Mr. Steinmetz, what goes on in that house of yours?"

"What goes on?" Steinmetz repeated, puzzled.

"The neighbors say there are strange lights and noises in the middle of the night."

"Oh, that," Steinmetz chuckled. "Yes, they are right. I have my laboratory in the house and I do experiments sometimes late at night. I have two laboratories; one is at the plant but this one here is for late at night. Come, come, I'll show you."

The sergeant discovered that the most imaginative neighbor had not exaggerated the scene. Upon entering the dark and cavernous front hall he was met with a slightly sulphurous odor, the result of electrical experiments. On one wall was a large panel of switches that controlled the lights in every room in the house. They were not the ordinary push-button type but industrial knife switches that seemed to threaten electrocution to anyone who came near.

At the far end of the hall was Steinmetz's physical laboratory that contained a clutter of high-voltage apparatus, transformers and rheostats and insulators and banks of wet and dry-cell batteries and a forest of wire leading in every direction. To the left of the hall was the parlor—no less cluttered, but with things less lethal. A large, round table was in the center of the room and on it were a book of logarithms, a half-dozen finely sharpened pencils, a ream of paper and a glass bowl holding a dozen long, very black and very strong cigars. Surrounding the table were glass-fronted lockers that reached from floor to ceiling and contained spare parts for electrical equipment, trays of geological specimens, a collection of Indian arrowheads, a few technical books, some family photographs from Breslau, Germany, and the ordinary commercial souvenirs of travel, including a small replica of the Statue of Liberty. On top of the lockers were a couple of elaborate beer steins, a few bottles of white wine, and a canoe paddle.

On the opposite side of the hall from the parlor was Steinmetz's greenhouse. It contained not the traditional display of beautiful and aromatic flowers but dozens of cacti. They were monstrous plants full of attacking spines and splinters. One misshapen, bulbous cactus was covered with needle-sharp white hair. Another was a snaky, winding horror with clusters of unnatural-appearing fruit growing like ulcers on its body.

The menagerie in the yard just outside the greenhouse was surrounded by a brick-and-iron fence. Here lived not only the alligators but also a Gila monster. The Gila monster was a sluggish but dangerous beast from the Arizona desert. It had a thick body covered with a splotchy and pebbly hide, a head and tail as blunt and square as the body, and when it flicked open a scaly eyelid, its glance seemed full of torpid evil. Its saliva was pure poison. Yet, when Steinmetz scratched its neck, as he did now for the police who observed from outside the menagerie wall, the Gila monster stretched and yawned and showed every evidence of pleasure and gentle gratitude.

At this moment two crows, outcasts of the bird world, descended from the sky to perch on Steinmetz's shoulders. The little man introduced them to the policemen as John and Mary. The birds cawed raucously in his ear and he murmured back to them. Then, with a mischievous smile, he said to the sergeant, "Anyone can understand the language of crows if he takes the time. I always know when John and Mary are hungry, or when they're upset about something."

"Yeah?" said a policeman. "And what are they sayin' now?"

"They are rather angry over so many strangers being here. Please, you must forgive their bad manners."

Forgiving or not, the police soon left and the little

hunchback went into the house, the two crows still cling-
ing to his shoulders and talking vehemently. Thus was
written another chapter in the neighborhood's growing
legend of Steinmetz.

At this stage no one could foresee that Steinmetz, more
than any other single man, was to be responsible for the
growth of the General Electric Company into one of
America's industrial giants. No one could guess that he
was to bring prosperity, fame, and a parade of the world's
great men to the city of Schenectady. The neighbors only
knew they lived next to an eccentric who surrounded
himself with ugliness. They saw that the more thorns,
prickles, fangs, scales, and claws an animal or plant had,
the better he seemed to like it, the more tenderly he cared
for it.

A few of them, a very few, guessed at the reasons for
this. Steinmetz was acutely aware of the impression his
twisted body made upon normal people; he had caught
the quick look of revulsion; he had heard the children
cry in fear, and he had firmed himself against the pain it
caused him. His menagerie was his way of saying that all
God's creatures need love, and if some of them are considered ugly, then they must love one another.

CHAPTER TWO

Give me your tired, your poor,
Your huddled masses yearning to breathe free,
The wretched refuse of your teeming shore,
Send these, the homeless, tempest-tossed, to me:
I lift my lamp beside the golden door.

THESE WORDS, inscribed on the Statue of Liberty, greeted twenty-four-year-old Karl August Rudolf Steinmetz with particular aptness in the spring of 1889. Few men who sought a new start in the New World were as tempest-tossed as he.

True, Steinmetz had never looked worse than on that June day when the steerage passengers of the French ship *La Champagne* were finally herded ashore after two days' wait at anchor while the upper-class passengers were being processed. He had caught a bad cold during the trip over and his face was swollen badly to make him look even less presentable than usual. As he stepped before his interrogator he drew himself up in a pitiful attempt at dignity.

"Your name?" snapped the official.

"Karl August Rudolf Steinmetz."

The official made a laborious job of writing it down, thus emphasizing its foreignness. Finally he was ready to bark his second question: "Profession?"

16

"Mathematiker und Forscher."

The official frowned in annoyance. He understood German but he didn't approve of anyone's speaking it. "Do you have money?" he demanded.

Steinmetz stood silent. He guessed it was damning to be without funds, and his pockets were absolutely empty. He didn't wish to lie this first day of his new start, and his silence told the truth. The official made a note to the effect that he was without funds.

"You speak English?" was the next question.

"A few," came the hesitant answer.

"No English," the official commented, writing it on a form. Then he demanded, "Do you have a job in America?"

Steinmetz didn't understand this question and the official angrily repeated it in German.

"Nein," Steinmetz finally replied.

The official walked over to his superior, pointed out the forlorn Steinmetz and said, "He can't speak English, he hasn't got any money, he hasn't got a job, he's sick, and he's a hunchback!"

The superior nodded. "He can't come in."

The official waved Steinmetz out of line and pointed toward a door over which was a huge sign that bellowed, in a dozen languages, DETENTION PEN.

What the immigration officials did not know—nor would they have altered their ruling if they had—was that among all his other problems this young man was a political refugee. To return him to Germany meant his immediate arrest and imprisonment.

Steinmetz's involvement with Bismarck's police came

about in this way. He had been born in 1865 in a brick apartment house on the outskirts of Breslau, a neighborhood that was mostly middle class, Protestant in religion, conservative in politics. A middle-aged Bismarck, five years from the assumption of full power, could not have anticipated that opposition was being bred in such a neighborhood. However, the developing political climate and the circumstances of Steinmetz's life combined to place him in eventual opposition to the arrogant and aristocratic "Iron Chancellor."

The day of his birth was an emotional one in the apartment. His father paced nervously in the living room while the mother was attended by a midwife. After some hours the child was born, wrapped in flannel, and carried into the living room. The father noted the child was lying in an awkward position and demanded, "Is . . . is he healthy?"

"Oh, yes," the midwife assured him. "The left leg isn't quite straight and there is a small hump on the back, but he'll live all right."

The father closed his eyes in pain and turned to walk away. And as he walked he dragged his left leg slightly and there was a hump on his back . . . just as there had been on his father's before him.

Within a very few years it became apparent that if nature had given this child an imperfect body, it had compensated by giving a mind that was more than first-rate. When he was eight and a half years old he entered a classical gymnasium (the equivalent of an American high school) and immersed himself in Latin and mathematics. In his second year he studied logic and French;

in his third, Greek and philosophy, Polish and dialectics and Hebrew. He learned his Horace and Homer so thoroughly that for the rest of his life he could recite long passages from the ancient poets. He became a linguist, proficient in five languages but not, ironically, in the one he was so desperately to need on Ellis Island when he was twenty-four.

At seventeen years of age Steinmetz graduated from the gymnasium with such high marks that he was excused from the traditional ordeal of an oral examination. That fall he enrolled in the University of Breslau.

His choice of a university was what shaped his future career, for Breslau was one of the very few schools that bothered to include the study of electricity in its course of physics. No school in all of Germany had a course in electrical engineering, and few students even attended the electrical lectures in the Breslau physics course. Yet, that was the field to which Steinmetz gravitated with single-minded enthusiasm. He didn't then dream he could have a career in a science so insignificant; he only knew that it fascinated him beyond all power to turn aside to more popular studies.

Three years earlier Thomas A. Edison had brought out his incandescent electric lamp, and Nikola Tesla, twenty-six, was now beginning research that was to lead to a radical new motor and a system for transmitting electricity over great distances. The world was on the doorstep of the electrical age. Steinmetz appeared at the right moment in history.

German undergraduate life was gay and lusty. Great emphasis was placed upon physical prowess and there were clubs dedicated to mountain-climbing, swimming, rowing and, of course, dueling. A saber wound on a young man's face was a badge of honor proclaiming that his courage had been tested.

The deformed young man who hitched himself shyly about the campus the first days of the term was obviously not a candidate for any of these clubs, but he was determined not to be cheated out of all social life. He met all eyes with a tentative but ingratiating smile and after the first shock of his appearance had worn off, he received smiles in return. He even received an invitation to join a student club, the mathematical society.

The members of this society had a deep interest in mathematics; being young, they were also dedicated to beer-drinking and revelry. One night each week they met in the back room of a restaurant at eight o'clock and for two hours drank beer and held learned discussions about their academic speciality. At the end of two hours, songs replaced discussion. By midnight the society had dwindled considerably, and by 2 A.M. only a handful remained. This small group usually adjourned to one of the "Vienna cafés" to drink coffee until morning. Steinmetz was one of the few always to greet the dawn.

It was not only to win acceptance that Steinmetz stayed with the revelers; he enjoyed every minute of it. His ordered and intense mind needed relaxation in frivolity, and within his frail body there was a lustiness of spirit that won the respect of his fellows. Before the first college year was half over he knew he had carved himself a place in campus life. It may not have been a position of complete equality, but it certainly was one of special affection. He learned the terms of his acceptance during a ritual meeting called by his society for the purpose of giving each member a nickname.

It was the tradition that the senior members of the society give the first-year men a nickname by which they were to be called for the duration of college. Often the name stuck for a lifetime. Steinmetz set out for the meeting with some misgivings, for he had heard that frequently the names were not tender.

The first-year men were lined up before the society and one by one called forward to be named. Steinmetz was third in line and much too nervous to hear what the first two were named. When his turn came he stepped three paces forward, clicked his heels and came to attention. His twisted little body made a parody of Prussian formality.

The chairman looked at him, smiled and raised his stein. "Half a glass to Proteus," he intoned. "Proteus the versatile, the ever-changing, who knows economics, classics, and mathematics, who can answer questions on every subject."

"To Proteus!" the assembly echoed and lifted their steins.

Steinmetz bowed and sat down, determined to keep all emotion from his face. Flattering words had accompanied the name, but he knew the Odyssey from beginning to end. According to Homer, Proteus was a prophetic old man of the sea who was full of wisdom and could discourse on all things past, present, and future. He lived in a cave on the island of Pharos, near the mouth of the Nile, and he could change himself into many shapes; now a lion, now a serpent, a leopard, a tree, even fire and water. But his human body, to which he always returned, was that of an old hunchback!

For better or worse, Steinmetz was to be called Proteus for the rest of his college years. Perhaps there was some cruelty in the nickname, but there was truth in it, too. It was a truth he could not escape, a truth he carried on his back for all to see, a truth he had to live with, preferably with good grace.

For the rest of the evening young Proteus answered quickly and easily to his new name and told a great number of jokes.

In the 1880's Germany was making a rapid change from a feudally organized agricultural country to a modern industrial state, and the transition was accompanied by harsh political coercion. The "Iron Chancellor" Bismarck had little use for democracy and all opposition was met by columns of goose-stepping soldiers and prison sentences. The country seethed with resentment and revolt, much of it centering among the faculties and students of the universities. Steinmetz, preoccupied with mathematics, remained naively unaware of the ferment until his second year.

Introduction to the underground opposition came to him from a most unforeseen quarter. One of his close friends was a student named Henry Lux, nicknamed Hinz. Hinz was a member of the mathematical society and a part of the small group that visited the Vienna cafés after the meetings. He was the gayest of companions, singing in a fine baritone voice and having a great supply of quips and jokes. He was thought to be slightly superficial, perhaps, but a diverting companion and always welcome.

It was after one of the all-night rounds of the cafés that Steinmetz discovered how he had misjudged Hinz. They were walking slowly back to their rooming houses in the early dawn, walking slowly because Steinmetz could not walk fast, and Hinz was suddenly quiet and apparently deep in thought. Several times Steinmetz was aware of receiving a long and measuring look from his companion and at last the silence was broken.

"Karl," Hinz said, refraining from the Proteus nickname that had been used during the evening. "Have you given much thought to politics?"

"No," Steinmetz admitted, "I haven't."

Hinz slowed his step and glanced behind. The streets were empty in all directions, yet the young man went through the ritual of avoiding eavesdroppers. When he spoke again his voice was low, conspiratorial. "We have a Socialist club in town, a study group, and I think you would find it most interesting. Some remarkable people belong and I've been talking to them about you and everyone has agreed to invite you to our next meeting. You'll hear some challenging ideas, Karl."

Steinmetz was not only flattered at the thought of people discussing him, he was also eager for "challenging ideas." He accepted the invitation.

Two nights later he and Hinz set out for a middle-class residential section of town and again there was the ritual of avoiding nonexistent eavesdroppers, spies, and agents provocateurs. It was quite melodramatic and by the time they arrived at their destination and Hinz rapped a special signal on the house door, Steinmetz's pulse was fast with excitement.

The door was opened first a crack, then wide. They stepped inside. Eight people, divided equally among college students and townspeople, were drinking tea in the small parlor and Steinmetz received a flatteringly warm reception. He knew the students by sight on campus. Of the townspeople he learned that the man dressed in a cutaway was a successful physician; the man with calloused hands was a bricklayer; the man with the gold pince-nez was a private tutor and the woman a housewife. Despite their various and prosaic backgrounds, they were all welded together by an ideal that lifted them out of themselves, made them appear wiser than they were, braver than they were, stronger than they were.

Theirs was not the harsh, class-war dogma of Karl Marx, but the old-fashioned socialism that visualized a brave new world in which there would be no war, no poverty, no exploitation of man, no hate. That night Steinmetz became a Socialist. He was nineteen years old.

The University of Breslau required six years of study for a degree. For five and a half years Steinmetz did brilliant academic work and his professors prepared to graduate him with highest honors. Throughout this time he continued to work with the Socialists, speaking and studying—and for a time even editing their local newspaper, *The People's Voice*. Membership had grown slowly but enough so that the college students were able to form their own club, independent of the townspeople's association.

In Steinmetz's final year the club did something that revealed that, for all their secret passwords and secret knocks and whispered conversations, they were not really revolutionary Socialists at all, but college boys playing at it. Included in the club were two medical students who were leaving Breslau to complete their studies in a large hospital. A farewell meeting was to be held and it was decided to commemorate the occasion by having a group photograph taken. They made an appointment at the studio of a commercial photographer and upon arrival two members were carrying a large and very heavy package. They removed the wrappings to reveal a marble bust of Ferdinand Lassalle, the deceased founder of the German Socialist Party.

"He's a member of our club, isn't he?" demanded one of the students.

"Of course he is!" came a chorused reply.

"Then he should be in the picture, shouldn't he?"

Again there was enthusiastic agreement. There were nine members of the club and when they grouped for the picture, five sat in the front row on chairs, and four in back with Lassalle's bust in the middle.

A print of the picture went to each club member and then the photographer asked to display it in his shop window. The club granted permission.

This bravado did not escape the vigilance of the Imperial German government. The police knew that Lassalle was the founder of the Socialist Party, and they naturally concluded that the young students grouped around the marble bust had embraced the outlawed doctrine. The photograph was confiscated and a relentless drive undertaken to identify and find grounds for the arrest of every man in the picture.

The young hunchback was perhaps easiest of all to identify, and suddenly Steinmetz discovered he was being shadowed. The police questioned his friends and associates. They studied *The People's Voice* to clip and study the articles that came from his pen. Slowly and carefully they put together evidence that would imprison him. In February 1888 they had their case and were ready to move.

Just as they were on the point of arresting him, Steinmetz's friends learned of the plan and dashed to warn him. They told him that he had to leave the country, or most certainly face a long prison term if he stayed. He was on the threshold of completing a notable university career and about to receive the highest honors with his degree. To flee now was to surrender all he had worked so long and hard to achieve. It was a bitter choice, made no more palatable by the sudden knowledge that he didn't really want to be a politician at all. He was, in heart and mind, a scientist and he wished to be left in peace to study. But it was now too late to alter the course of events he had set in motion.

His mother was dead but his father still lived in the old apartment, quietly going about his work and bearing the pain of his own deformity in silence and dignity. Steinmetz went to him before dawn, sat on the edge of the bed and gently woke him.

"Father, I'm going out of town."

The little man sat up quickly, blinking the sleep from his eyes. "Is anything wrong, Karl?"

"No, nothing at all. I'm simply going to visit some college friends and I have to catch an early train."

"How long will you be gone?" The father was not entirely reassured.

"Only a few days. I'm sorry I woke you up but I didn't want you to worry."

"All right, Karl, I won't worry," the father promised. "But take care of yourself."

They embraced and then the young man quickly left. He walked quickly and jerkily to the railroad station and stepped aboard a train headed for the Austrian border.

He spent a miserable, poverty-stricken year in Zurich, Switzerland, eking out a living by tutoring the children of wealthy families and writing occasional scientific articles. He made friends with a Dane by the name of Oscar Asmussen, and when that young man decided to go to America in the spring of 1889 he had little difficulty convincing Steinmetz he should go along. Surely, Steinmetz thought, the New World would not be so harsh a place as the Old.

But he didn't reckon with the officialdom of Ellis Island.

CHAPTER THREE

THE IMMIGRATION OFFICIAL pointed toward the Detention Pen and barked, "In there to await deportation as an undesirable alien."

Steinmetz didn't understand all the words, but the gesture was unmistakable and so was the significance of the room to which he was being sent. Deportation to Germany, to Bismarck's police, to prison, and all because nine high-spirited young men had posed for a photograph with a marble statue!

During this dialogue, Oscar Asmussen had been busy with another official some yards away. Now that he had been cleared for entry, he turned to look for his friend and found him shuffling dejectedly toward the Detention Pen.

"Karl . . . Karl, where are you going?" he cried.

"I am to be deported as an undesirable alien," Steinmetz said dolorously.

"Ha!" Asmussen snorted. "We'll see about that."

Asmussen was no older than Steinmetz but he was a world traveler and more sophisticated in the ways of the petty bureaucracy. Assuming an arrogant and patronizing manner, he said to the immigration official, "Mr. Steinmetz is one of the most distinguished mathematicians in Europe and is here to consult with certain American concerns about various electrical phenomena." At this point he removed a large roll of bills from his pocket. "I am carrying his money for him. We have several appointments in New York, so please approve his admission promptly."

The admission was approved and as the two friends walked out of the building and toward the ferry that would take them across the harbor to Manhattan, Steinmetz exclaimed, "Oscar, what did you say in there? What magic words did you use to get them to change their minds?"

"I said you were a rich and distinguished scientist."

"Ach," said Steinmetz, "I have no money at all. I do not even know where I shall sleep tonight."

"I have relatives in Brooklyn. We'll move in with them for a while."

"You think they will welcome me, a stranger?"

Asmussen threw his arm around his friend's narrow back and laughed. "Didn't you know that all Danes are crazy?"

The relatives in Brooklyn welcomed Steinmetz just as if he too were a Dane. They not only sheltered and fed him during the first weeks but gave him English lessons so that he might be better equipped to look for a job.

His first application was to the Edison Machine Works, where he was promptly turned down.

"It seems to me there is a regular epidemic of electricians coming to America," the plant superintendent grumped. A few years later the General Electric Company, offspring of Edison's manufacturing companies, was to bring some of its most difficult problems to Steinmetz, but now the young man was turned from the door.

One letter of introduction was in Steinmetz's pocket. It had been written by a Mr. Uppenhorn of Munich, editor of a German electrical publication to which Steinmetz had contributed articles during his exile in Zurich, and it was addressed to a Mr. Rudolf Eickemeyer who owned a small manufacturing firm in Yonkers, New York. After his rebuff at Edison Machine Works, Steinmetz took a train to Yonkers.

He found a begrimed three-story brick building in an unlovely part of town by the railroad tracks. Encouraging, however, was the fact that the hum of machine tools came through the open windows. There was work here; the only question was whether it would be shared with the young refugee.

The office clerk, the owner's nephew, looked up from his desk when Steinmetz entered, and a frown went across his face. He saw a man wearing the roughest of clothes on a deformed body. Above his bearded face was a tattered cap.

"I should like to see Mr. Eickemeyer, please," Steinmetz said.

To his own surprise the nephew found himself climbing the stairs in search of his uncle. When he found him he said, "There is a strange-looking fellow in the office asking to see you. He looks as if he just jumped a freight train. I can send him away."

"I'll see him in a moment," Eickemeyer said.

Eickemeyer, who entered the office a few minutes later, was in striking contrast to his visitor. He was a tall and formidable man with the full beard of a patriarch and he looked sternly down at Steinmetz. A man passionately dedicated to his work, he did not easily suffer interruptions.

Calling upon his carefully rehearsed English, the visitor said, "I am Mr. Steinmetz. Do I have the honor of addressing Mr. Rudolf Eickemeyer?"

For all his impatience Eickemeyer was a compassionate man and he said gently, *"Sprechen Sie Deutsch?"*

Steinmetz smiled his gratitude and spoke German, producing his letter of introduction. Eickemeyer read the letter and began eagerly to question Steinmetz about the latest electrical developments abroad. The two men talked intensely, almost excitedly, for two hours. And a week later Steinmetz reported for work on his first job in America. He was to be a draftsman and his pay was to be twelve dollars a week. He was ecstatic.

Steinmetz and Oscar Asmussen set up a bachelor apartment near the Yonkers plant and both began to save money. Steinmetz wanted to pay off his debt to his friend, and Asmussen needed money to bring his fiancée over from Europe. In a short time both men had achieved their goals, and they broke up their apartment, Asmussen moving west with his new bride.

Before parting, however, a significant event occurred in Steinmetz's life. He burst into the apartment one evening to announce it to his friend.

"Oscar . . . Oscar! I'm going to become an American citizen."

"Congratulations!" his friend exclaimed.

"I just decided this afternoon. If I'm going to make

my living in America I think I should be an American."

"I know your new country will be very proud of you," Oscar said.

"Let's hope you're right. But one thing I know already, I'm proud of my new country." He smiled wryly. "There are no Bismarck police here."

The following month he appeared before the Bureau of Immigration and Naturalization to take out his first papers. He was given a form to fill in and the very first blank was for his name. He thought that over for a long time, his pen poised. Karl August Rudolf Steinmetz was his name, but he didn't write it down. It sounded so German and he was becoming an American. He would keep his last name, Steinmetz, of course, but he decided to anglicize Karl, and for his first name he wrote down Charles. What about a middle name? Suddenly, without consciously willing it, he saw the pen form the word Proteus. He looked at the name and smiled with wry and affectionate memory. Proteus, the old man who could assume many forms but who was a hunchback most of the time by choice! He let the name stand and, with a flourish, completed his signature:

Charles Proteus Steinmetz!

CHAPTER FOUR

NOT IN ALL America could there have been a better job
for Steinmetz than the one he got in Yonkers. Not only
was he propelled into that branch of electrical science
that was to lead him to his great successes of later years,
but he found in Rudolf Eickemeyer an understanding
friend.

Like Steinmetz, Eickemeyer had had a youthful brush
with an autocratic German government and fled to America following the revolution of 1848. He became part
businessman, part scientist, and part philosopher. The
two men spent many hours exploring and comparing their
egalitarian convictions and soon Steinmetz became a regular Sunday afternoon and evening guest at the large
dinner parties in Eickemeyer's baronial home, Seven
Oaks.

Eickemeyer was trying to develop heavy-duty electrical motors for industrial use and the assignments that
went across Steinmetz's drawing board those first weeks
revealed the diversity of his experimentation. On June
10, 1889, Steinmetz was told to make an assembly drawing of Eickemeyer's detailed drawing of a motor for an
electric car. On June 22 he began to make drawings,
according to his journal, for "a switch for overhead con-

ductor." The following month he was given the job of drawing plans for electric streetcars. From July 11 to July 13 he worked on an electric water pump, and the week after that he was busy with fourteen-inch and twelve-inch dynamos.

In August, Eickemeyer told Steinmetz to draw the design for a motor intended to operate a "vertical trolley" or an "elevator." This was at the request of Norton P. Otis, who was eventually to organize the Otis Elevator Company. The motor that Eickemeyer designed and Steinmetz drew was shunt-wound, the first of its type ever produced.

But of all the projects undertaken, the one that intrigued Eickemeyer most was that of designing ironclad dynamos and motors of sufficient size and power to propel a trolley car. This was a wildly radical idea at the time, for the public was firmly convinced that Old Dobbin hitched to the front of the car was more reliable than anything Eickemeyer and Steinmetz could produce with wires and iron. And the public was almost right!

Eventually three electric streetcars were equipped with the motors built in Eickemeyer's Yonkers factory. They were operated in Sunday trial runs on the Steinway Road in Brooklyn. This novel venture brought crowds of passengers and scoffers. They got their money's worth! Hardly a day passed without one or the other of the cars breaking down and being hauled ignominiously back to the barn for repairs.

There was one particularly vexing problem: the trolley-wheel at the end of the pole, forming the contact point by which the electric current traveled from the feed wire to the motor of the car, could not be kept in place on the wire. First they tried two wheels, one on top and one on the bottom of the power wire, but this ran into all sorts of snags with supporting wires. They tried to magnetize the wheel, and thus "glue" it to the wire, but when the car started up it was discovered that the magnetism was not strong enough and the pole, wheel and all, crashed down on top of the car.

Steinmetz bent over his drawing board to grapple with the problems turned up by each Sunday's trial run, and gradually they were all solved—all but one, the basic one that had plagued electrical manufacturers for years, the motor itself. Each motor was built and, if it overheated, was torn apart and rebuilt. Mass production of large motors was impossible under these conditions.

All Steinmetz had been asked to do was make a drawing of a motor already designed, but he was a man aflame with scientific enthusiasm and he threw himself at the basic problem. Eickemeyer, to his everlasting credit, recognized genius and relieved the little man of his drafting chores and gave him a small electrical research laboratory of his own. It was here that Steinmetz made his first revolutionary discovery in electrical engineering and called it the "Law of Hysteresis." This discovery produced the first murmurs of his later thundering fame.

In most electrical apparatus magnetism is used [he said in explaining this]. Sometimes the magnetism remains constant, as in the fields of direct current machines; sometimes the magnetism alternates, as in transformers..

When the magnetism alternates, it consumes power. Such power consumption means loss of efficiency and results in heating. It is therefore of importance to the builder of electrical ap-

paratus to make the designs so that this loss of power by alternating magnetism (called "hysteresis") is as small as possible.

However, the laws of this power loss were entirely unknown at this time, and many engineers even doubted its existence. The designer of electrical apparatus simply built the apparatus, then tested it, and when the hysteresis loss was found too high and the efficiency too low, or the machine too hot, they tried again. This, obviously, was not a satisfactory way.

> ...I had to calculate and design an alternating current commutator motor, of the same type that was now used on the New York, New Haven and Hartford Railroad and other railroads. I knew there would be a loss of power in the alternating magnetism of the motor, and I wished to calculate this "hysteresis loss," to get the efficiency of the motor. I therefore looked through the literature obtainable and found two tables of hysteresis losses given, one by Ewing, in his book on magnetism, and one by Kapp, in his little book on alternating currents.
>
> Unfortunately, the two tables disagreed with each other very much, and the curves given by the tables differed in shape from each other.... From Ewing's table of hysteresis losses, however, I derived mathematically a law, the "law of hysteresis" showing how the hysteresis loss increases with the increase of magnetization. Roughly, it is that every time the magnetization doubles, the hysteresis loss trebles.
>
> ...I started testing...various kinds of materials which were available, various kinds of iron and steel, and gave these results ...before the American Institute of Electrical Engineers..

Steinmetz's words give no clue to the drama that attended his report. The AIEE meeting was scheduled for January 19, 1892, and attendance was light, for there was no indication that anything out of the ordinary was to happen. A strange-looking little man was scheduled to give a paper on "hysteresis," but no one had ever heard of the man or guessed the import of his paper. And things looked even less promising when Steinmetz took the stage.

His unpressed suit was ill-fitting, he had forgotten to remove an enormous pair of overshoes, and his pants were caught in the tops of them. When he began to read his paper, his voice was high in pitch, singsong in expression and overlaid with a heavy German accent. He was difficult to listen to, but what he said began to take hold of that meeting and electrify it. Every engineer present began to feel a personal excitement as he realized that that funny-looking little man on the platform was giving him a new tool to work with.

When the meeting ended there was loud applause and everyone crowded around Steinmetz to congratulate him. But the little man wasted no time basking in praise. The following day he returned to work on a second paper giving complete data on the magnetic characteristics of all magnetic materials then known. This second paper was presented to the Institute in September of that same year.

This time a large and eager audience was present. Frank Sprague, famous builder of electric railways and then president of the AIEE, introduced the principal speaker by saying, "His work in the past has been most important in its character and this paper will fully support the reputation he has already earned." The famous A. E. Kennelly of Edison's Laboratory said that the paper was "classic" and that the "Institute may well congratulate itself upon this paper having been read before it."

Eickemeyer was naturally pleased and proud of his young protégé's success. In the factory Steinmetz's relationship with his colleagues was unique—he attracted no jealousy. He had, within two years' time, supplanted many an older employee in the boss's favor, in salary, and in outside acclaim, yet there was no resentment of him. Steinmetz was completely without vanity, completely without a sense of status. He was as interested in every other man's job as he was in his own and often stopped to help a laboratory assistant wind a motor or solder a connection. There radiated from Steinmetz a loving good will and interest in all men, in all living creatures, and it was impossible not to respond to him.

One winter day an engineer from another concern came to consult Steinmetz about a problem and when he had climbed the three flights of stairs and entered the research laboratory, he was amazed to find the potbellied stove without fire and the little scientist working in overcoat, heavy cap, and boots. His hands were blue with the cold and from time to time he rubbed them briskly to return flexibility to his fingers so that he could manipulate a pencil.

They discussed the visitor's problem and Steinmetz made some suggestions that seemed to solve it. As the man was about to leave, he couldn't help asking the question that had bothered him all during the visit.

"Mr. Steinmetz," he said, "why don't you build a fire in the stove?"

"Oh, that?" Steinmetz exclaimed, as if aware of the cold for the first time. "A mouse had some babies in there and they are not yet old enough to move."

Three years to the month after his arrival in this country an event took place that was to have momentous consequences for both Steinmetz and America—the General Electric Company was organized. This new concern was determined to hire the best brains in the industry and had heard much of the young mathematician who worked for Eickemeyer. E. W. Rice, Jr., who was later to become General Electric president, was dispatched to interview Steinmetz and return an opinion on the advisability of hiring him.

Rice recalls the visit in these words:

I had read articles by [Steinmetz] which impressed me with his originality and intellectual power, and believed that he would prove a valuable addition to our engineering force.

I shall never forget our first meeting at Eickemeyer's workshop in Yonkers. I was startled, and somewhat disappointed, by the strange sight of a small, frail body, surmounted by a large head, with long hair hanging to the shoulders, clothed in an old cardigan jacket, cigar in mouth, sitting crosslegged on a laboratory work table.

My disappointment was but momentary, and completely disappeared the moment he began to talk. I instantly felt the strange power of his piercing but kindly eyes, and as he continued, his enthusiasm, his earnestness, his clear conceptions and marvelous grasp of engineering problems convinced me that we had indeed made a great find. It needed no prophetic insight to realize that here was a great man, who spoke with the authority of accurate and profound knowledge, and one who, if given the opportunity, was destined to render great service to our industry.

Steinmetz liked Rice. He was excited by the great plans General Electric had and he saw an opportunity for far greater research facilities than he could ever hope for in the tiny building in Yonkers. He agreed to go to work for General Electric if Mr. Eickemeyer had no objections.

But Rudolf Eickemeyer most certainly did have objections. He feared the loss of his young engineer would have disastrous effects upon his business and he strongly opposed the plan. Steinmetz again saw Rice and announced his inability to take the job.

"But why?" demanded Rice. "You were ready to take it last week."

"Mr. Eickemeyer does not wish me to leave," Steinmetz said simply.

"Now look here, Steinmetz, we're ready to bargain. We can raise your starting salary by a couple of thousand. How is that?"

"You're raising my salary?" Steinmetz exclaimed in amazement. "But why? Money has nothing to do with this. If you offered me ten times as much, that would not change the facts."

"What facts?" the exasperated Rice exclaimed.

"My responsibility to Mr. Eickemeyer. He gave me a job when I needed it badly. If now he needs me, it is my duty to stay with him. I am sorry, Mr. Rice, but those are the facts that money cannot alter."

The following month two other General Electric officials arrived in Yonkers to examine the Eickemeyer books and analyze his patents. They were not overly enthusiastic about either the sales record or the electrical patents held, but one asset tipped the balance sheet over-whelmingly into the black—Steinmetz, the genius whose work had impressed them so, was an Eickemeyer employee.

General Electric bought the Eickemeyer firm and thus Steinmetz became a General Electric employee.

CHAPTER FIVE

SCHENECTADY WAS a peaceful town slumbering beside the Mohawk River in upper New York state. It had been founded by the Dutchman Arndt Van Curler, and the mark of the early burghers was still clear. Everyone went to the Dutch Reformed Church. The paving stones of the street were large and flat, as in the Netherlands. There was an immaculateness of stoop and gutter, and the citizens went about their jobs at a dignified pace. The Erie Canal meandered through town, and on its waters barge traffic moved at two miles an hour.

All this changed in 1892 when General Electric was formed and came to town. Over the following years, acres of land in the heart of the city were flattened, and a series of large, six-story buildings rose in the air. They were of no discernible architecture, rather ugly to the eye, but they pulsated with the new energy of the twentieth century—electricity.

Young engineers, speaking a variety of languages, marched energetically through the previously tranquil streets. None was more alien to Schenectady, however, than the hunchback with the large head, bristly beard, and spindly legs. People turned to stare at him with cruel curiosity, but Steinmetz always continued on his way, puffing his cigar, giving no indication that he was aware of the glances. He was aware, of course, and acutely sensitive to the effect of his appearance. The only defense he put up was the unique one undertaken in his home, which he named Liberty Hall.

By surrounding himself with alligators and cacti and Gila monsters and crows, he declared himself on the side of nature's outcasts. He said to the town, in effect, "You may think us ugly but we know that surface appearance means nothing. We have the same reactions and needs as the rest of nature, and we can give the same love. If no one else will have our love, we'll give it to one another."

If he surrounded himself with strange cacti for his own psychological reasons, he maintained an objective, scientific interest in the plants. He wrote to a friend in the Smithsonian Institution at Washington: "I am, and always have been, very much interested in this family of plants for various reasons, not the least of which is their pronounced illustration of the laws of evolution and survival of the fittest.

"As the result of conditions being different from those of other plants in their desert life, to my mind they illustrate very interestingly adaption; by the change of the leaves to protective organs, the necessity of eliminating the large evaporating surface of the ordinary plant leaves which would not be permissible in the desert, the water storage in trunk and stem, the taking up of the breathing function of the leaves by the stem in retaining the chlorophyll therein, the channeled shape of the stems to get larger contact surface with the air without materially increasing evaporation, the large flower of the insect-fertilized varieties to secure fertilization under conditions where insect life is not very plentiful, night-blooming due to the more plentiful insect life of the desert during nighttime and also to escape the loss of the large amount of moisture which would result from maintaining a large flower open during the heat of the day, the mimicry of shape of some varieties, the protection by offensive juice of many families of similar habitation—Euphorbia, Aloe, etc. . . ."

Nothing that came under Steinmetz's eye was viewed for just its surface appearance. He always probed into structure and cause and significance. In truth, the whole world was his laboratory.

Having Liberty Hall and its weird occupants for neighbors was part of the price the good burghers of Schenectady had to pay for progress, for making their town an industrial giant. And there were many who claimed the price was too high.

If Steinmetz was rejected and even taunted by the town, things were just the opposite within G.E. He became the keystone of a brilliant engineering staff; he was the flame that ignited enthusiasm, inspired that final extra effort to achieve what appeared to be the unachievable. He accomplished this, not alone by his undeniable intellectual supremacy over all others, but also because of his great generosity in placing his talents at the service of any man and his problem. Steinmetz's laboratory door was always open and he would put aside his own exacting work to assist a visitor. The problems brought to him were not always strictly scientific.

One day a new employee, a young newspaperman

named Clyde Wagoner, presented himself at Steinmetz's door. He had heard the little man's reputation for giving sympathetic help to all callers, and he badly needed help. The scientist was in his usual position, standing with one knee on a stool, hunched over his desk, and he looked up to say, "Hello. Come in. What's new?"

"Mr. Steinmetz, I'm in trouble."

"Ah, so?" Steinmetz put down his pencil and shoved aside the figures he was working on. "Tell me what the problem is and maybe we can solve it."

Wagoner had a problem that threatened to get him fired from a job he had held less than a month. He had been a reporter for several major New York state newspapers and knew how difficult it was to obtain easily understood science and engineering stories from the nation's big industries. He had come to General Electric with the proposition that they hire him as a one-man news bureau to prepare and distribute concise and easily understood press releases about the discoveries and inventions being made by the new company. In his youthful enthusiasm he had declared, "Hire me and I'll get you a lot of front-page news stories."

He had been hired and the time had come for him to produce what he had promised. "Mr. Steinmetz," he explained, "yesterday my boss called me in and announced he had a terrific front-page story for me to send out. The story was that we've just sold a sixty-thousand-kilowatt turbine generator to Commonwealth Edison in Chicago. Well, golly, this may sound like big news to us, but not to the public. This story will get maybe a paragraph on the financial pages, but that's all."

"Hmmmm," said Steinmetz. "The problem is to get

the story on page one and thereby save your job. Right?"

"Yes, sir," Wagoner said bleakly. "But there's nothing dramatic about a generator."

"Nothing dramatic? Well, let's see." Steinmetz picked up a pencil and began to figure rapidly on a fresh sheet of paper, talking to himself as he did so. He murmured, "A sixty-thousand-kilowatt turbine generator produces the energy of eighty thousand horsepower. Each horsepower is equal to the muscle work of twenty-two and a half men; therefore, eighty thousand horsepower equals one million eight hundred thousand men. However, men cannot work twenty-four hours a day, while our generator does. Therefore, we multiply the generator manpower by three eight-hour shifts and we find it produces as much energy as five million, four hundred thousand men. Now then, the slave population in 1860 was four million seven hundred thousand. Ha!"

He threw down his pencil and turned to the disconsolate young man. "I suggest you send out a story that says we are building a single machine that, through the miracle of electricity, will each day do more work than the combined slave population of the nation at the time of the Civil War."

In these dramatic terms, the giant turbine generator *did* make the front pages of all the newspapers in the nation, and Wagoner kept his job and later went on to build for General Electric a news bureau that brilliantly pioneered industrial reporting.

As Steinmetz's reputation for helpful and cheerful accessibility grew within the company, there were many men who offered friendship. But he was shy about such relationships; his deformity was something always before him and he had built his own protection with alligators and cacti. He made it clear to himself, and to his associates, that he did not help men with their problems to buy friendship. But slowly he dared to let himself see that he had a circle of friends despite his attempted rejection of them. He discovered that a group of young scientists had come to him, not because he was the most brilliant of them, not to receive, but to give of themselves. He discovered that they liked him!

Now that his wall of loneliness had been breached, he experienced a flood of emotion he little knew how to express. The old habits of shyness and self-protection could not be altered at once, if at all, and he could not clap a man on the back and speak gratefully of comradeship. All he was able to do at first was to respond in a burst of rather juvenile horseplay and practical jokes. And the ordeal was not confined to his circle of cronies but imposed upon anyone who came to visit him at Liberty Hall.

The mere approach to the gloomy structure was unsettling enough, for a visitor had first to pass the outdoor menagerie and be subjected to the baleful inspection of the alligators and the Gila monster. A heavy iron knocker on the large, dark double doors echoed hollowly inside, and after a moment the doors parted to reveal the small, misshapen master of the house. There was a pixie smile of welcome on his bearded face, but to a visitor with imagination it could be construed as something diabolical.

At the far end of the hall could be glimpsed the physical laboratory with its clutter of high-voltage apparatus;

to the right was the greenhouse with rows of predatory ferns and twisted, spiny cacti and a sandbox of scorpions and snakelike eels in a pool.

The visitor was usually guided to the left, toward the double doors leading to the parlor, and upon grasping the knob on those doors he'd give a cry and jump in the air while his host chuckled. The door handle was wired to give a mild electric shock. Within the room the visitor was seated in a large chair opposite a floor-to-ceiling mirror.

After a few moments of conversation the visitor would feel a tingling sensation in the seat of his pants and then see his frightful reflection in the mirror. Every hair on his head would be standing straight out!

"Don't be alarmed," Steinmetz would say quickly. "It's only static electricity." Then he'd pull a switch, the chair would be de-electrified and the visitor's hair returned to his head.

If the visitor happened to be a woman, Steinmetz delighted in switching on an overhead mercury lamp and she would look in the mirror to see her black lips parted in horror over skeleton-white teeth.

Steinmetz's half sister, Clara, came from Germany to visit him and promptly installed herself as housekeeper. She did not at all approve of the easy bohemian way in which Steinmetz and his friends lived. Ernest Berg, Steinmetz's assistant at General Electric and his roommate in Liberty Hall, was a practical joker who resisted all of Clara's efforts at reform. When Ernest's brother Eskil arrived from Europe to work at G.E. and join the Liberty Hall hijinks, Clara gave up her attempts to bring order and decorum to the house and announced she was moving out. She was not urged to stay. Despite their difference in temperament, however, Steinmetz felt both fondness and responsibility toward Clara and took care of her financially throughout his life.

Fortunately for everyone, Steinmetz's practical joke period soon ended and he and his cronies settled down to long evenings of wine and talk. Sometimes they played poker, Steinmetz organizing what he called The Society for the Distribution and Equalization of Wealth. He was a formidable poker player, especially in stud, for his mind could instantly calculate the odds against filling any given hand.

This gay, bohemian life included picnics and outings along the Mohawk River, costume parties, and even projected glider flights. One evening Steinmetz said to his friends, "I have here a few shares of a new company I know you will all want to get in on. It is the Mohawk River Aerial Navigation, Transportation and Exploration Company, Unlimited. Not everyone can buy this stock, only those who have two dollars."

"What's it for?" his friends demanded. "What do we get for our two dollars?"

"I have been studying the dynamics of air currents and I believe I can design a glider that will carry us all up and down the Mohawk Valley. The money from the stock will finance the purchase of materials to build the glider."

The money was eagerly subscribed, not only by his regular cronies but by other associates at General Electric, and he went to work on a fabric and wood set of wings to be strapped to a man's body. The result was complete and utter failure. On several Sundays Steinmetz and his friends went to Hoffman's Hill just outside of Schenectady, strapped on the wings and ran down the hill to launch themselves in air. The only results were bloody noses and skinned knees.

In his enthusiasm Steinmetz had brought along his camera to record the soaring success of his creation. There was no success and he could only take a picture of a winged friend standing on the ground. However, he retouched the picture to remove the hill and make it appear that the man was in midair with the skyline of Schenectady superimposed below. He sent this picture to all stockholders.

"Such a remarkable picture is worth the two dollars they invested in the company," he said.

To most observers Steinmetz must have seemed a happy man. His work at General Electric was going spectacularly well. He was completing his studies of alternating current which helped revolutionize American industry, and he had a happy-go-lucky social life with a close circle of friends. What more could a man wish? Well, Steinmetz, in common with most men, *did* wish something more of life. He desperately wanted a family of his own. And at the same time he had firmly denied himself the right. He was the third generation of hunchbacks in his family and he early decided the twisted genes were too strong for him to take a chance in having children. He could not inflict on a child the emotional suffering he had endured. He decided to end his family line with himself.

He had the iron will to enforce such a decision, but it

was beyond his capacity to stifle the longings for family that frequently swept over him. At such times he would have traded places with the lowest clod of a man, if that man had a wife and children around his table each night.

Knowing he would have no children of his own, he went to endless efforts to make friends with the neighborhood children. He took them through his laboratory and menagerie when they were brave enough, which was not often, and he always stopped to talk to them on the street as he went to and from work. He added a big dog to his house and let it be known that if the dog ran away he would pay fifty cents reward for its return. It became a neighborhood game to lure the dog to the next block, then decide he was lost and take him by the collar to return him to his master.

Though this would occur a dozen times a week Steinmetz always paid the reward and sat on the front steps of Liberty Hall to talk to the child as long as he would stay. The children thought they were putting something over. They could not understand his need.

CHAPTER SIX

WHEN STEINMETZ CAME to work for General Electric he was deep in his research on the nature and behavior of alternating current, and his new employer gave him the time and equipment and the encouragement to continue.

Up until this time most electrical generating systems, including that of Thomas Edison, had used direct current. Direct current flows continuously in one direction; it can be measured in amperes, and its characteristics are constant and easily controlled. There was one drawback to it (and a big one!). By means of knowledge and equipment then available, direct current could not be transmitted economically for a distance of more than three miles. The nation could never be electrified if a generator had to be installed every three miles from coast to coast. Steinmetz—along with a handful of engineers such as George Westinghouse, Nikola Tesla, and Elihu Thomson (whose Thomson-Houston Company had become part of General Electric)—was convinced that alternating current would solve the problem.

One major trouble with alternating current, however, was the difficulty of calculating its intensity and effects. Alternating current does not flow continuously in one direction. As its name implies, it alternates, flowing first in one direction and then reversing itself and flowing in the opposite direction. As generated for purposes of light and power, it changes its direction at the rate of 120 times a second, but for radio and other special purposes it may reverse itself thousands or even millions of times a second. During these changes, its value fluctuates from zero to maximum, back to zero again, and again back to maximum.

To measure alternating current, and to design generators, motors, transformers, and power lines that could use it, engineers had to make complicated and time-consuming calculations. These involved not only the direction and intensity of the current but also the element of time.

It was to help simplify these tantalizing and often seemingly insoluble problems that Steinmetz now bent all his efforts. He was not an inventor like Edison, but a mathematician. Edison and his associates had invented a working light bulb, but they could not grapple with the problems of alternating current. Steinmetz's tools were a flat tin box full of sharp pencils, reams of paper, and his own mind that could perform the most amazing calculations, often without even the use of his two other tools.

At last he announced that he had solved these problems by means of mathematics which substituted symbols of his own invention for more complicated conventional formulas. Because his method was completely new, he first had to teach his fellow engineers how to use it. But once they had learned, they were able by means of it to design alternating-current machinery and transmission lines more rapidly and more effectively than ever had been possible before.

Such influential electrical pioneers as Edison and Lord Kelvin fought bitterly for the continued use of direct current and against the introduction of alternating current, but the decision made by the Cataract Construction Company in 1893, to use alternating current for the first large-scale harnessing of Niagara Falls, soon ended the battle.

The original contract called for three generators of 5,000 horsepower each, utilizing an advanced alternating-current system (which employed not merely *one*, but *two* or *three* separate alternating currents) patented in 1888 by Tesla. These produced electricity at two thousand volts, and this was stepped up to ten thousand volts by transformers. Then the current was carried over bare copper conductors on wooden poles with porcelain insulators to the city of Buffalo. There another set of transformers reduced the pressure back down to two thousand volts again at a substation.

When, in 1896, the switch was thrown for the first time, the generators hummed, wires sang, and a great city had electricity produced at an unheard-of twenty-six miles away! In the face of this demonstration all opposition from the direct-current partisans melted away and soon power was transmitted, not just twenty-six miles, but thousands of miles across the continent. The electrification of the nation had begun.

Every time a man rode a streetcar, or took an elevator, every time a housewife's tired arms were spared by the willing motor in her washing machine, every time a farmer's well was pumped and his fields irrigated, every time a great industry built factories and created a future for men, women and children, it was with the assistance of alternating current. Electricity became the burden bearer of the race. And modest Charles Steinmetz, a man pathetically eager for acceptance as a human being, had played a brilliant part in helping to bring this about.

The mathematical logic that Steinmetz employed to achieve practical production and distribution of alternating current was so subtle that few engineers could understand it, even after hearing a lecture on the subject. To explain his theories, to enlighten new generations of electrical engineers, Steinmetz decided to write a book. The book, packed with close and involved reasoning, eventually grew to three, and these were only the forerunners of a whole series of scientific writings produced by the little genius.

Steinmetz's publisher was the McGraw-Hill Book Company, already well established at the turn of the century in the publishing of engineering and technical books. By 1917 McGraw-Hill had published eight of the scientist's books. They were *Alternating Current Phenomena; Theory and Calculation of Electric Circuits; Elements of Electrical Engineering; Engineering Mathematics; Radiation, Light and Illumination; Transient Electric Phenomena and Oscillations; Electric Discharges, Waves and Impulses;* and *Theory and Calculation of Electrical Apparatus.*

Steinmetz and his publisher had a happy relationship that lasted twenty-five years, until his death. During this time he carried on a lively correspondence with McGraw-

Hill, taking great interest in the details of book production—quality of paper and illustrations, choice of type faces, design and binding. The publisher was proud of this distinguished author, who undoubtedly attracted to the house other important writers of scientific and technical works. Indeed, several came on his personal recommendation.

In writing these books, as in all his laboratory work, Steinmetz employed a shorthand of his own devising. He developed his system as a student in Germany and perfected it as he learned to speak and write English in America. Its foundation was the Swedish Arends system, combined with the best of several others and then modified to his own needs. The underlying principle was phonetic. He wrote the word *height* in three letters: *h-i-t.*

His system was a terror to strange secretaries who might be suddenly called on to transcribe it, but once learned, it was simplicity itself. Steinmetz was enormously pleased with it, and boasted, "It is like swimming. . . . With other systems a person who does not use it for a year or more is likely to forget the greater part of it. But my shorthand is simple, and as readable as longhand. I can read today notes that I took forty years ago, and read them as easily as those I took forty minutes previously.

"My experience has taught me that shorthand is of great advantage, especially to students. The work becomes simple with shorthand, since the student's attention is not distracted from the speaker by his writing, as is often the case when one attempts to make notations in longhand."

Steinmetz contended that his system of shorthand enabled him to write as fast as he could think. And certainly his pages were marvels of grace and neatness, full of the dashing loops and spirals of the old Spencerian school. He could load one sheet of paper with enough material to result in three pages of typewritten manuscript.

One of his small disappointments in life was the fact that he was never successful in popularizing his shorthand method in the schools. He considered it (or any shorthand, for that matter) a valuable and time-saving research tool for all students in all fields.

Under the impetus of Steinmetz's discoveries, General Electric expanded and Schenectady prospered. The citizens were not unaware of the identity of their benefactor and now when they turned to look at him in the streets it was with respect and gratitude. Along with Edison and Marconi and Einstein, the nation's newspapers were making him a celebrity, and the townspeople proudly pointed him out to visitors as "our Steinmetz."

A grateful employer increased his salary manyfold, which was gratifying but essentially unimportant to Steinmetz. He had little interest in money for its own sake, and it could buy little that he really wanted. His real reward from General Electric was the freedom to conduct any research he chose, to do it in his own way and in his own time. The company supplied him with all the equipment he desired, both for his office and his home laboratories, and all the assistants he needed. "Lab boys," young men doing apprentice work at the plant before receiving responsible positions, were eager to assist Steinmetz and the brighter ones were given the privilege.

Steinmetz conceived the idea of establishing a research

laboratory not only to service the expanding product division of General Electric and handle their specific problems but also to delve into the vast unknown of electricity.

This idea of establishing a laboratory devoted exclusively to scientific investigation was revolutionary. No other industrial concern in the world had such a laboratory. Such work was being done at universities, of course, but not by a company engaged in production. However, the G.E. management's faith in Steinmetz was such that they approved his plan without hesitation. He and his laboratory became the "Supreme Court" of General Electric. Whenever an engineer had a theory he wished to explore or a project to undertake and it required an outlay of funds, the company always said, "Go to the Supreme Court. If he says that there's something to your idea, we'll give you the money and the men."

Steinmetz became idolized by his lab boys, not only because of what they learned from him, not only because he was gentle and considerate in personal relations, but in addition because he was their champion before management.

E. W. Rice, Jr., by now president of the company, learned this one day shortly after he had decreed another raise in salary for Steinmetz. His secretary put her head in his office door and said, "Mr. Steinmetz would like to speak to you for a moment."

"Send him in," Rice said with a wave of his hand. He was going to be thanked, he knew, and it is always pleasurable for a man to hear such words. "Ah, Steinmetz," he exclaimed when his door opened again, "come in, come in."

The little man entered the office, dressed as he always was for work—a turtleneck sweater, a pair of baggy pants and a long cigar. He came directly to the point. "You have given me a raise in salary."

Rice smiled deprecatingly. "Yes, we have."

"I have not earned it."

"Indeed you have, Steinmetz, every penny."

"No, no!" He shook his shaggy head. "Since the last raise I have done less work, not more. It is the lab boys who deserve the raise. I want you to take this money and divide it among them."

"That's quite impossible," Rice said.

"Why?"

Rice struggled to frame a diplomatic answer. What he wanted to say was that it was nobody's business what the company paid its employees, but he didn't say that. He managed with, "It is our opinion that the lab boys are adequately compensated for the work they do."

"You are wrong," Steinmetz said.

This impasse held for several moments while the two men looked at each other across the broad desk. Steinmetz finally shrugged his thin, crooked shoulders and said, "I will accept no more increases in salary until the lab boys receive one." Then he hitched himself out of the office.

Such an ultimatum from an employee would be laughed at by most large companies, but not in this instance. Anything that happened to Steinmetz was a headline. The newspapers were constantly speculating on Steinmetz's salary, variously reporting that he was underpaid, that he was overpaid, and that each week he was given a blank check on which he wrote his own salary. The last thing the company wanted now was to get into a front-page controversy with their most famous and most valuable asset.

Another thing that haunted the management was the fear that a competitor might one day hire Steinmetz away. His loyalty was well known. General Electric had had to purchase Eickemeyer to get him, yet someone might succeed in luring him away with a good offer *if* he was unhappy. There was the key to the situation. Steinmetz must be kept happy, even if it meant letting him dictate salaries for other employees.

The following week the raises were announced. No one could prove it, but the lab boys were convinced that Steinmetz was the man who had somehow wangled it for them. Who else, they reasoned, cared about them?

Among the lab boys assigned to Steinmetz was a lanky young man with a shock of blond hair that kept falling over his forehead; a quiet, unruffled, earnest manner; and the name of Joseph LeRoy Hayden. There had been, perhaps, more brilliant assistants than Hayden, but none had suited Steinmetz's work habits and temperament so well. He could take an assignment and research it thoroughly, keep accurate records, draw the proper conclusions, and forget all about time in the process. The two men seldom watched the clock; they ate when hungry and slept when tired. As soon as these two interruptions had been disposed of, they returned to their work.

The young man had another quality that endeared him to the older: he was a good listener. *Everyone* listened when Steinmetz spoke about scientific matters, but Hayden listened when the little man spoke of personal things, when he reminisced about Germany. He saw the loneliness in Steinmetz and responded with sympathy and interest. He, of all the associates and friends, guessed what it was like to live a hunchback. No word about the physical deformity was passed between them, but this was not necessary. There was an empathy that let them communicate without words.

The relationship became close very slowly, for Steinmetz distrusted intimacy. To give bits of himself to another human was to make himself vulnerable and dependent, and that was frightening. This particular friendship developed almost despite Steinmetz.

At this time he was working on a new arc light for city-street illumination. He was researching the possibility of a magnetite lamp and explained his reasoning in a memo to G.E.'s patent department:

"For 25 years, carbon has been exclusively used for terminals in the arc lamp, although carbon is the most unsuitable material, since the carbon arc gives practically no light, and whatever light the lamp gives merely comes from the incandescent tip of the positive carbon. In the magnetite lamp neither of the terminals is sufficiently hot to give light by incandescence, but all the light is given by the conversion of the electric energy into light in the metal vapor, which is carried off from the negative terminal by the current."

Even after its successful development, the magnetite arc did not come into general popularity at once, for it required direct current. To solve this new problem, Steinmetz proposed to make a demonstration installation at his own house. He had a small powerhouse built on his lawn and installed a Brush machine to supply the direct current of four amperes at three thousand volts. There were twenty-five lamps in the installation, each mounted on a pole, and when they were finally hooked up and turned on, they threw a bluish green light over the grounds and the assembled spectators, who were thrilled and applauded wildly.

After a year or two Steinmetz conceived an improvement on his giant lamps. Up to now the power for them was supplied by Brush machines, direct-current generators designed by a G.E. associate, Charles F. Brush. But Steinmetz discarded these cumbersome machines and substituted a mercury rectifier. This rectifier, which also proved of great value in charging storage batteries, was made for constant-potential low voltage and high current. This simplification of power supply immediately popularized the arc lamp and it was installed on many street corners in many cities.

Several years of research were required to develop this light. To achieve maximum concentration, Steinmetz did most of the work in a new laboratory he had built on Wendell Avenue on the edge of the city. He planned to build himself a home there eventually, but at this point had only completed and equipped a two-story laboratory. The lab had its own power generator under the care of LeRoy Hayden.

Often the two men worked through the night and had to wait in the early dawn for the first streetcar to take them back to their homes. Steinmetz finally suggested that they place two cots on the second floor of the lab and sleep there nights. He volunteered to do the cooking, thus eliminating the necessity of leaving the lab at all. It was agreed.

Steinmetz now pushed forward the construction of his long-delayed house. He had only rented Liberty Hall and once the bohemian life had palled a bit, he wanted a home of his own. He went over the plans with LeRoy Hayden, asking his advice and agreement. The building was to be a large, three-story structure of brick with peaked gables, in Elizabethan style. There was to be a menagerie and a greenhouse, all of it attached to the already constructed laboratory.

As the building began to take shape and the two men supervised every step of the construction, Steinmetz admitted to himself that he had come to look upon Hayden as the son he had never hoped to have. He had denied himself the right to think about such a relationship, but here it had crept in upon him and absorbed him with a wonderful warmth and trust and security. Truly, for the first time since childhood, he did not feel alone. He dared not yet reveal these thoughts to the young man; he could only express them in an exuberance of work. Never had Steinmetz been as happy as this fall and winter.

A great blow came to Steinmetz on a rainy day of the following spring. It was staggering, not so much because it was a surprise as because it was not. It was the thing he had secretly feared might happen, something he had tried to brace himself to meet.

During a coffee break Hayden said with a forced casualness, "I'm going to get married."

After a long moment Steinmetz was able to form the word and repeat it. "Married?"

"Next month, if it's all right with you."

"Married," Steinmetz said again.

"You've met her. Corinne Rost."

"Oh yes, yes, of course."

"I don't want to disrupt our work any more than necessary and I told Corinne she'd have to find us an apartment near the lab."

"You'll be moving out of here? Yes, of course."

"We don't plan a very long honeymoon, a week at the most."

"Take as long as you wish," Steinmetz said in a faraway voice.

Hayden leaned over and touched the little man on the arm and said gently, "This won't affect our work together."

Steinmetz smiled a little crookedly and said, "Of course not. It won't change a thing. Not a thing."

berty Hall. The alligators escaped from the outdoor pen at the right.

(Left) The beginning of Steinmetz' cacti collection in Liberty Hall. The plants eventually grew so large that they almost took over the house. *(Right)* One of Steinmetz' pet crows perches on the window sill at Liberty Hall

The Wendell Avenue home with Steinmetz' laboratory and greenhouse

(Left) Grandchildren Midge and Billy experiment in Steinmetz' laboratory with "Daddy" nearby. *(Right)* Midge and Billy in the orchid house

(Right) Steinmetz and his adopted family at Christmastime

GENERAL ELECTRIC

(Below) Dr. Steinmetz on his bicycle in winter

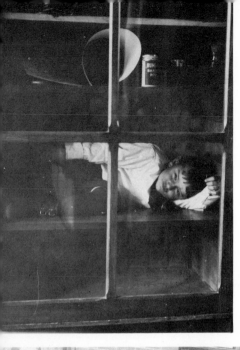

(Left) Grandson Joe, a "rare specimen" in Steinmetz' display case

(Below) Steinmetz, his "family" and his electric automobile

(Above left) Camp Mohawk   *(Right)* Supper at Camp Mohawk
(Below left) The famous work table at Camp Mohawk   *(Right)*
Steinmetz at work in his canoe

A mirror shattered by lightning at Mohawk. By fitting together the pieces of this glass jig-saw puzzle, Steinmetz learned the characteristics of lightning

(Below) Steinmetz demonstrates artificial lightning in the laboratory

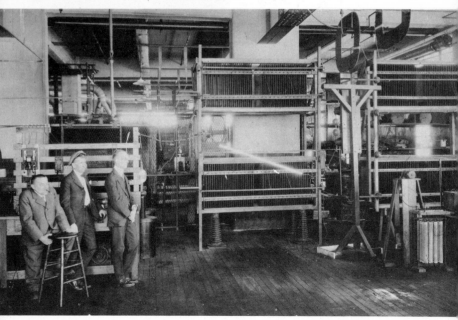

(Above) Marconi visits Steinmetz at the G.E. plant in Schenectady

(Below) Steinmetz and Edison confer

The Electrical Genius at his desk

CHAPTER SEVEN

THE CONSTRUCTION of the big Elizabethan house continued and each day Steinmetz wandered among the carpenters and masons and plumbers without the bird-quick interest he had previously shown, without searching questions about craft and quality of material, without last-minute changes in the plans. It was as if he were walking through a house ghost-haunted even before its completion.

As the peaked gables took shape the vast proportions of the house became visible; it dwarfed all others in the neighborhood. Steinmetz's associates, as well as his new neighbors, speculated on the house. Why had a bachelor built such a structure? He couldn't occupy all the bedrooms. The vast center hall, the dining room, the parlor, the library, the butler's pantry and the greenhouses were of dimensions that would allow no single person comfort. It was a house that had to be populated to be useful, or even endurable.

Steinmetz himself had no clear understanding of what had motivated him. He had wanted a home of his own, and he had the money to build a *proper* home, not a cottage, so why not do so? He never admitted to himself the existence of the hope, the superstition almost, that if he surrounded himself with the paraphernalia of a family, then the family itself might appear.

During the last week of May 1903 LeRoy Hayden married Corinne Rost and took her on a short honeymoon trip. When they returned to Schenectady they moved into a small apartment on Park Avenue near Steinmetz's property on Wendell Avenue. Steinmetz observed their coming (he had spent a good part of each afternoon watching the apartment) and quickly returned to his laboratory to await Hayden. But apparently the young groom had decided his honeymoon was not ended until the following morning. Steinmetz found he could not wait the final few hours, and after some fidgeting, he walked to the small apartment and knocked on the door.

Hayden's face broke into a warm grin of welcome and he turned to call over his shoulder, "Honey, guess who is here?"

"Mr. Steinmetz," came the reply, and if there was a slightly acid tone in the bride's voice, the groom did not notice it.

"Come in . . . come in," he boomed. "Golly, I've been wondering how things are going at the lab. Did you finish charting that last arc phase?"

"Some remarkable characteristics were revealed," Steinmetz said. "I've been anxious to discuss them with you."

The two men sat down, lighted cigars and filled the tiny living room with smoke and talk. Immersed in the technicalities of their work they lost all track of time and as it grew dusk, the bride finally interrupted them to say briskly, "It's suppertime."

The men looked up from their conversation with momentarily blank faces as they reoriented themselves. Steinmetz murmured his disbelief and went through the ritual of his two watches. He always carried a cheap watch and an expensive one, and never checked the time without consulting them both. If there was a variance in their report he quite logically took the word of the expensive one, theorizing that better materials and more careful workmanship deserved more reverence. Why did he carry the cheap one at all? It seemed to serve as a rough sort of policeman to keep its elegant relative honest.

After consulting the watches and finding it was indeed suppertime, Steinmetz climbed reluctantly to his feet, murmuring, "I had no idea I had stayed so long."

"Honey, do we have enough food so Mr. Steinmetz could stay for supper?"

For a moment Corinne Hayden stood stiffly in the middle of the room, without answering. The men looked up at her, waiting her word. Then suddenly she saw them as they were—two small boys who had been interrupted in play. True, their play was important scientific work, but their attitude was the same as two boys who had been building sand castles. They looked at her with eager, half-pleading expressions.

She relaxed and smiled and said in a gentle, motherly voice, "Of course, Mr. Steinmetz may stay for supper."

During dinner the two men resumed their earnest conversation without directing a single word to her, just as she knew they would. And after that, Steinmetz had supper with them every evening.

Corinne Rost Hayden, a handsome, well-built woman of French-Canadian stock, possessed a clear, no-nonsense view of life. She knew from the first that Steinmetz was going to be a problem in her marriage. She was willing to share her husband with his work but not to the degree that Steinmetz seemed to demand. She saw, much before her husband did, that the lonely little man was trying to live in them, through them, trying to create a family for himself. She watched the big house rise and knew that would be the bait. She did not dislike Steinmetz. He was too giving of affection for her not to give some in return. Nevertheless she was determined not to have her life and her family absorbed by an outsider.

Hardest to bear was the loneliness of the battle, for she could not make her husband understand what was at stake. She finally had to conclude that he was at least a passive partner in Steinmetz's campaign.

The day the house was completed Steinmetz took Le-Roy and Corinne Hayden on a tour of the rooms. The third floor held a series of small rooms for servants, the second floor a horseshoe of grand bedrooms, the first floor the imposing entrance hall with its sweep of stairs, the parlor and dining room, the library, the attached greenhouse and office; all of it was empty and full of echoes as they marched through the rooms.

Finally Steinmetz turned and spoke to Corinne. "Why don't you come and live with me?"

"No," she said. "Thank you, but no."

He gestured about the vast establishment. "There's so much room here. It would be pleasant for everybody."

"Our apartment is adequate for us. It is kind of you, but no."

She turned and walked away and there was no more discussion that day. It was not the end of the subject, however. Steinmetz did not again state his case, but her husband did. There *was* some rough logic to it. The house *was* large, and the two men did work late at night and how convenient it would be to live in the same building with the laboratory. They could never afford to live in such a grand scale on their own—why not take advantage of the generous offer?

"He is a German!" Corinne snapped at her husband during one of the arguments.

"What in the world do you mean by that?" he demanded.

"I mean simply that he has a German point of view about women. In his eyes we are sufficient for bearing children and cleaning the house, but that is all. He does not consider our feelings because he seems to think we have none. We are not worthy of serious conversation because we have no intellect either. In his eyes all women are servants. Well, I won't be his!"

For the first time in their marriage she wept and then ran to her room and shut the door. As in all family quarrels, the hot words held elements of both truth and untruth. Steinmetz, having eliminated women from his life, did not understand them, was ill at ease with them, and certainly gave the impression of patronizing them. He was not the martinet Corinne thought him, but on the other hand he was determined to have his way in this case and his pressure was unrelenting. He wanted a family with a desperation that blinded him to the harm he might be doing to a marriage.

Corinne could not win against the two men, but when she saw surrender was inevitable she determined to obtain the best possible terms. She went to Steinmetz and said bluntly, "If we move in with you I must run the house as I see fit."

Struggling to conceal his elation, Steinmetz said, "Of course, my dear."

"You'll give me an allowance for your share of the food and I'll shop and prepare the meals I consider proper and nourishing."

"Indeed."

"The meals will be served on time. You and Roy will leave the laboratory when they are ready."

"Absolutely."

"There will be a strictly business arrangement about money. You will pay your share of everything, but nothing more."

"Whatever you say."

She could think of no more demands and turned about to march back to her small apartment and pack.

After she was gone, Steinmetz allowed himself a triumphant smile. At last he had a family! To be sure, it was one with some built-in stresses and strains, but what family is without them?

CHAPTER EIGHT

STEINMETZ DIDN'T KEEP his promises. He meant to, but some of them were simply beyond his ability. He couldn't stop in the middle of an experiment just because it happened to be time for a meal. He just couldn't do it. Nor could he always tear himself away from his magnificent new greenhouse when Corinne announced that the food was on the table. There were times, in her frustration, when she went and got him by the arm and led him into the dining room. He'd come, uncomplaining and with a sheepish smile on his face.

He was absent-minded about almost everything not immediately touching on his work in progress. He'd forget appointments with prominent people, he'd forget to take a bath, to change his clothes, to get a haircut. Corinne found herself taking on the duties of secretary, nurse, and mother.

Then there was the problem of money, and that was the most difficult of all for her to deal with. Her stiff pride demanded that she and her husband pay two-thirds of the household expenses, but this was almost impossible of achievement. Steinmetz found a hundred little ways to give luxuries and increase their standard of living. One day she was in the kitchen when he marched in with

71

that combination of bravado and guilt which told her at once that he had bought something.

"Surprise!" he exclaimed.

"What now?" she demanded, wiping her hands on her apron.

"Come outside and see."

He ushered her outside and with a comic-opera bow, pointed to a most impressive sight—an object made of cut-glass vases holding artificial rosebuds, of plush upholstery, of silk curtain shades dripping with tassels. It stood tall and square and ponderous with dignity—an electric automobile. Corinne was impressed despite herself and clapped her hands together. Steinmetz grinned happily.

"Who is the car for?" she demanded sternly after recovering herself.

"Oh, I thought we . . ." he paused and changed the sentence. "I thought that I needed one."

"But you don't drive."

He waved his hand. "Someone will drive it."

She stood speechless, completely unable to cope with this sort of indirection, and finally shrugged her shoulders and went into the house.

Steinmetz's attitude toward money was that of a man who was completely immersed in an exciting life's work, doing what he would do even if he were not paid for it. To Steinmetz it was amazing that he should receive so much money for doing research that was its own reward. Since his own wants were minimal, he used the money to bring happiness to others. What else was it good for? It took Corinne some time to realize that the gifts forced upon her and Roy were not bribes but the acts of a generous and loving heart.

Steinmetz's largess was not confined to the family but was showered upon any man with a hard-luck story. Hardly a day passed without some such person presenting himself at Wendell Avenue. Corinne tried to protect Steinmetz and whenever she answered the door she sent them flying, but they soon learned to take their transparent tales of woe around to the laboratory door. The little scientist never failed to answer their knocks, never sent them away empty-handed.

One day Corinne saw a particularly disreputable-looking character make his way through the yard, but before she could get to the laboratory to head him off, he had Steinmetz's ear.

"And there she is, gov'ner, lying sick abed," he was saying in a dolorous voice. "A fever she's got, my poor little daughter. I don't know what's wrong with her, but if I don't get her to a doctor she won't live out the day."

Steinmetz was already reaching for his wallet.

"Ya don't know what it does to a father's heart, gov'ner, to see his own suffer and not be able to lift a hand to help."

"How much is the doctor's fee?" Steinmetz asked.

The man considered carefully and then said, "Three dollars." As three one-dollar bills came out of the wallet the man added hastily, "There's the taxi fare, gov'ner. Doctor don't come to a poor man's house, you gotta go to his office. And I couldn't be carryin' my poor sick daughter on a tram, now could I?"

"How much for the taxi?"

"Cost a full dollar." He watched another bill being

added to the three, then said quickly, "One way, that is, gov'ner. Cost me another dollar to get my poor sick child home again."

When five dollars were offered he paused, but could think of no other reasonable contingency, so he accepted the money. "Bless you, gov'ner, bless you," he murmured. As he passed Corinne, trailing his nimbus of rye whiskey, he wore a sly and triumphant grin.

Furious, Corinne turned on Steinmetz and cried, "That story about the sick child was ridiculous. He's taking that money right downtown and drinking it up. How can you be so blind? Don't you realize that you're aiding and abetting that sort of irresponsibility by giving handouts to every man who comes here with a hard-luck story?"

Steinmetz was contrite, yet unyielding. He nodded his head and said, "You're right, of course. Absolutely right. And yet, don't you see, my dear, that there may be one man who comes to my door who really needs the money? I can't run the risk of turning him away."

Slowly the young wife came to understand that she had in her keeping a truly unusual human being. Seeking nothing for himself, he was generous, he was loving, he easily accepted other men's faults (if they were not scientific!) and he was unfailingly cheerful. Never did he bring a bad mood to the table; never did he speak a word in impatience or anger. He was a sunny companion who occasionally still indulged in a practical joke. There was perhaps a bit more subtlety in his jokes now than before; at least there was in his revenge on Major Andrews.

Major Andrews lived at the end of the block on Wendell Avenue and was as opposite from Steinmetz as another human could be. The Major was the self-important commander of the Schenectady National Guard and he had regard for the male body only when it was straight and tall and dressed in a military uniform. Next to giving military orders he liked best to groom his front yard. His lawn was like a putting green, his front hedge stood at attention, and his favorite flowering quince tree dutifully showered him with blossoms and fruit. He pridefully marched his domain, unaware that fate was preparing an invasion from the other end of the block.

Enamored of automobiles, Steinmetz had now bought himself a second one—a Stanley Steamer. On this afternoon he left his laboratory to take a relaxing stroll around the grounds and he came upon his two cars standing side by side in the driveway, the sedate electric and the raffish Steamer. At this moment he developed an urge for a ride, but no one was home to chauffeur him. He had never driven but he had watched LeRoy and knew it was only a question of steering. Any fool could calculate the proper arc to go around a right angle corner. Yes, today he'd drive himself.

Again he studied the two cars, then in a burst of unfortunate bravado he fired up the Stanley Steamer.

The two of them, monstrous car and birdlike man, rolled out of the driveway and down Wendell Avenue. When they came to the end of the street the driver calculated the turn with fine mathematical skill and they swept in a fine arc to the left. But midway through the turn something happened, something froze the mind or the muscles of the driver, and the car never straightened out. It continued the arc up over a sidewalk, ripped a hole through an impeccable hedge, plowed furrows across a green lawn and came smack upon a flowering quince, snapping it in half. The quince's revenge was to puncture the automobile's boiler and steam shot into the air with a great hissing. Neighbors peered out of their windows to look at the wounded beast and its dismayed master.

Major Andrews came raging out of his house and, in his best drill-field manner, ordered Steinmetz off his property. But it was not so easy, for the Stanley Steamer was impaled on the quince tree. A tow truck had to be sent for and during the wait the Major berated the hapless Steinmetz. As the audience of neighbors grew, the greater became the Major's arrogance, the more cutting his vocabulary. He gave full voice to his opinion that Steinmetz was a menace in an automobile; he even hinted that the little man might be a menace to national security. He implied that a man with a beard could not very well be a true blue American.

Throughout it all Steinmetz stood, cowed and humiliated. He could think of no defense.

After an interminable time the tow truck arrived to rescue car and man. Safely home, Steinmetz had to admit to himself that the Major had been right about his driving ability and he vowed he would never again drive a car. Still, he couldn't help feeling some resentment over the words the Major used to express his opinion. He plotted revenge.

His Detroit Electric was fitted out with dual controls, one set for the front seat and a second set for the rear. Each morning that he went to his downtown office at General Electric, he climbed into the electric to come careening around the corner of Wendell Avenue with his hands on the controls in the most nonchalant manner. And each time this happened, Major Andrews' apoplectic face appeared at his window as he steeled himself for more ruined hedge and lawn. The Major never learned that the car was being safely operated by the lab boy sitting so innocently in the rear.

The relationship between Steinmetz and Corinne improved steadily, not because he changed but she did. She laughed at his jokes and was patient with his absent-mindedness and tried to be forbearing about his extravagances. She became less and less self-conscious about her anomalous position in the household. She saw that Steinmetz and her husband shared a world she could never enter, and she ceased being resentful of her exclusion. She was a level-headed young woman who would have had a successful marriage under conditions far more onerous than these. And also, about now something happened that made the outer world seem a little unreal and certainly not very important. A baby was born.

Red and wrinkled and crying, the baby lay beside his mother in the upstairs bedroom, but his wails were music to her ears and to her visitor's. Steinmetz admired the lung power, marveled over the mechanism of the tiny fists, commented on his resemblance to ancestors, though surely there was none in such a squinting, angry face. Then, just as suddenly as he had started, the baby stopped crying. He smacked his lips tentatively a couple of times and when no food came his way, he went to sleep.

The silence hung in the room several moments while Steinmetz squirmed in his chair. He had something to say and though he had spent a good deal of time formulating his sentences he could not now remember them.

"Mousie," he finally said. Once, after one of her flareups, he had called her that as a joke, but the name had stuck and had become one of affection. He started again and this time completed the sentence. "Mousie, I want to adopt LeRoy as my son, legally."

She was not surprised, for she and her husband had discussed this development the night before. But now she too was full of inarticulate emotion.

Steinmetz could not bring himself to plead his case; he merely said, "I . . . I've talked to LeRoy and it's all right with him, but I won't do it unless you approve."

She looked up from her son and smiled at the anxious little man. Then she held out his hand to Steinmetz and said gently, "I approve, Grandpa."

CHAPTER NINE

TO BE A CHILD is to believe in belief. It is to turn pumpkins into coaches and mice into horses; it is to know the secret woods where elves speak; it is to make of nothingness everything; and too, it is to be surrounded by overwhelming adults who do not believe.

The three Hayden children, Joe, Midge, and Billy, were not entirely surrounded, for there was an adult in their family who did believe—their grandfather, "Daddy" Steinmetz. Of course, there was a time when they were not certain he really was an adult. He was no taller than Joe at nine years, and when they sat down to dinner, with Mother and Father at the head and foot of the table, four heads barely cleared the plates. The fact that one of them wore a beard didn't seem to make him any less childlike.

However, the mere fact of having a body of small dimensions does not let one automatically penetrate the illusive but defended boundary of childhood. Even seeing and believing is not enough. The primary credential is enthusiasm. Steinmetz had that in abundance.

Whether it was a game, a hike, some building project, a swim in the Mohawk River, or just sitting under a tree and imagining, Steinmetz's enthusiasms matched the children's own inexhaustible supply. And at a birthday party he topped them. He'd be up at dawn to decorate the house and hide prizes, and when the guests arrived he'd plunge into the middle of the squealing, milling crowd of children, laughing with them and urging them on to new exuberances.

And at some time during each party a moppet would cry out, "Daddy, show us some magic."

Joe, Midge, and Billy Hayden called their father Father and called Steinmetz Daddy. All the neighborhood children called him the same name, and the cry would be taken up by everyone at the party—"Daddy, Daddy, show us some magic."

"Sure, sure. I got some special magic," Steinmetz would cry happily. "Just follow me."

A bent and tuneless Pied Piper, he led the happy, dancing children out of the parlor and down the long corridor that ended at the laboratory. The mere entrance into this great room left them awed, excited, frightened, and full of desperate bravado. On all sides were retorts, test tubes, beakers, Bunsen burners, vials of chemicals, coils of copper wire leading to massive electrical equipment, and over all a slightly acrid smell.

Steinmetz turned to his audience and affected a conspiratorial air that sent new shivers down the young backs. He selected a large beaker of crystal-clear glass, filled it with a colorless fluid. Then he added a second colorless fluid and it all turned an amazing yellow; when a third fluid was added it turned a deep purple; and a final fluid returned it to amber. *Oh*s and *ah*s came from the up-turned faces, and Steinmetz, who knew all the logic of the chemical reactions, at this moment found it no less magical than his audience.

"I'll make you a knight on horseback!" Steinmetz cried.

"Yes . . . yes, a knight on horseback!"

He filled a bucket with water and placed it on the floor. Then he placed a ladle over a Bunsen burner and dropped a chunk of lead into it. When the lead had melted and swam shimmeringly in the ladle, he put on an asbestos glove, lifted the ladle and poured a single drop into the bucket of water. There was a violent hissing and sputtering as the hot lead spread and froze into a fantastic shape. All the children looked down into the bucket and a boy cried, "That's not a knight! It's a battleship."

"Perhaps you're right," Steinmetz said thoughtfully. "Let me try again."

A second drop of lead, a second spitting and sizzling, then a child cried, "It's a goblin . . . a goblin!"

Drop after drop of lead formed all the things the children could imagine—dragons and princes and castles and mountains and wolves—and they vied with each other to be first to name the object.

"How about some fireworks?" Steinmetz cried.

"Fireworks!" they echoed shrilly.

From a jar in the supply cabinet he took a lump of a silvery metallic substance, cut off a few small pieces, and sprinkled them into a pail of water. As soon as the sodium came in contact with the water, hydrogen was released in wild explosive bubbles that burst into colored flame. Never were fireworks so spectacular!

At the end of the long party day LeRoy Hayden and his wife might be understandably tired of their offspring and wish them early to bed and out of sight, but not Steinmetz. Even the most strenuous day did not suspend the routine of his telling a long bedtime story. No man or event was allowed to alter this.

One time Henry Ford, then at the first flush of his fame as creator of the Model T Ford, came to Steinmetz with a problem. His automobiles had headlights that ran from a magneto, and this source of power was reliable enough when the engine was racing but faded away to nothing when the motor idled. For all his mechanical genius, Ford had been unable to lick this and sought Steinmetz's advice. The famous man was invited to have dinner with the family and afterward he and Steinmetz retired to the office in the rear of the house. They were deep in the problem, their heads together, when the door burst open and in tripped Midge in her pajamas.

"It's time for a bedtime story, Daddy," she said brightly.

Steinmetz nodded, stood up and said to Ford, "It's time for a bedtime story. I'll return in half an hour."

Ford was shocked. He was not a man who tolerated interruptions, especially from small children, and he immediately revised his estimate of Steinmetz downward. If there had been a train out of town at that moment he would have taken it, but instead he walked the streets of Schenectady for half an hour and reluctantly returned to the Wendell Avenue house. It was fortunate for him that he did, because when Steinmetz came down from the bedtime story he quickly sketched on a pad of paper the solution he had devised for the lighting problem.

Steinmetz installed slides and swings on the front lawn and this became the playground for the neighborhood children. Their cries never disturbed him in his laboratory; they brought him refreshment instead. Whenever he was fatigued from a concentration of work, he had but to join the children in the yard for a half-hour or so and then return to his desk with new mental vigor. In these children he had found at last his personal security. These boys and girls had grown up with his own grandchildren and found nothing strange in his appearance. They knew he was different from other adults but someone they saw every day could not be strange. And so they did not stare, they did not snigger or taunt; they merely accepted. Blessed acceptance.

Steinmetz's associates began to remark on the fact that some of the lines were disappearing from his face, and that his humor had lost most of its old acid. There was a gradual change in his menagerie, too. As the alligators and Gila monsters died off, they were replaced by dogs and cats. His greenhouse was no longer dominated by cacti—he took up the growing of orchids. He stopped surrounding himself with ugliness, for he no longer felt ugly.

Now content and secure, he divided his waking hours between two worlds. Part of the time he was deep in mathematical calculations so complex that few other living souls (save Einstein) could conceive of them. During the remainder of each day he plunged into the simple, sunny, uncomplicated world of childhood. The intermediate world where most adults had to dwell, a world that included envy, greed, and selfish ambition, was as alien to him as if he had come from another planet.

CHAPTER TEN

FAME CAME inevitably to Steinmetz. He did not court it, and when it arrived he did not accommodate it. He did not change his manner of dress or thought; he remained the gentle, eccentric, simple man who happened to be a genius. And yet he could not entirely resist the pressure of his fame; it became the fulcrum on which he was pried out of his isolation.

He was elected president of the American Institute of Electrical Engineers. He received an honorary Master of Arts degree from Harvard, and during the ceremonies President Eliot said, "You, sir, are the foremost expert in applied electricity of this country and therefore of the world." And from Union College in Schenectady he received an honorary degree of Doctor of Philosophy. He had been robbed of his college degree in Germany by Bismarck's police; now at last he had received it in America. Henceforth he was Doctor Steinmetz.

Invitations to speak flooded Wendell Avenue; he accepted very few and generally those asking him to appear before scientific societies. He did not have a polished platform manner; he spoke in a high, accented voice, but he knew it was the content of his speech that was important.

One by-product of his fame intrigued him very much, however. He received a number of invitations to teach. Some of the offers came from famous universities and involved high fees and impeccable status, but typically he did not accept them. He decided instead to become Professor of Electrical Engineering at Union College, a small institution in Schenectady that could afford to pay him nothing. Geography had something to do with his decision, for Union College was only a few blocks from his Wendell Avenue home. He would not have to leave his family and his laboratory; he would not be altering his life, merely expanding it.

He was a Doctor, but he was soon to be Herr Professor. What wonderful echoes of Breslau that title set up in his mind!

There had been no engineering course in Union, and establishing a new department meant that he also had to establish basic academic policy and curriculum. He had very definite ideas and told the college trustees, "The first condition which the college should fulfill is to turn out educated men and not merely trained artisans. To devote the total college course to engineering studies presupposes that the general culture studies required for any educated man are completed when entering the college. But neither graduation from the modern high school, nor the entrance conditions of the college comprise a sufficiency of general culture studies, and therefore, a part of the . . . [engineering course] . . . must be devoted to them if graduation from college should be qualification of educated men. I am strongly of the opinion that a good general knowledge of English, literature, history and natural sciences and possibly at least one other language, is of far more importance and value, for the future success of the engineering student, than instruction in the numerous details of his special profession."

The curriculum was established for both an undergraduate and a graduate course, and the day approached when Steinmetz was to teach his first class. Excitement ran through the campus, for both faculty and students were well aware of the honor being bestowed upon their school. Fifty students had enrolled for the new engineering degree and they crowded the classroom to capacity as Herr Professor entered briskly on his spindly legs, took his place before the blackboard, and began.

For a few minutes there was confusion among the students, then disbelief, and finally dismay. Steinmetz had plunged into a complicated mass of figures like a diver disappearing into a whirlpool. From time to time he may have come up for air, but if he did, the students missed it. His rapid, high-pitched voice dealt with concepts the students had never heard of, and all the time he furiously scribbled symbols on the blackboard in a size too small for anyone beyond the first row to see. The cascade of meaningless words never stopped. The students became numb.

When Steinmetz's back was turned some of the bolder students slipped out the door; a few went out the window. Minute by minute the class shrank without the professor appearing to realize the fact. Actually, his attitude was the old German one that a teacher taught and a student learned if he wanted to. There was no question of duress.

The class was two hours long and the custom was to

take attendance at the beginning of the second hour. Steinmetz went through the process, his nearsighted eyes close to the student list. His ears heard "Here" called out after each name was read. When he finished the roll call he put down the book, and looked up to give the class a wry smile. "Twenty-five men are here," he said, "yet fifty answered the roll call. Gentlemen, a remarkable phenomenon." The classroom burst into relieved laughter.

In the months ahead Steinmetz tried to slow and simplify his mind to undergraduate level, but he was never completely successful. Only the most brilliant students could understand more than a fraction of what he taught. And yet he was a great success. He was that rarest of teachers, one who inspires. No student was able to watch the little man on the platform, bursting with enthusiasm and performing chalk miracles and leavening it all with shafts of humor, without becoming infected with the desire to know, the ambition to become.

Too, they saw a reflection of themselves in him. Just as he was a child with his grandchildren, he was in many ways an undergraduate on the campus. He shared his students' enthusiasms, he never missed an athletic game, his humor was on their level, and most unifying of all was the fact he was a nonconformist.

Hardly a month passed without some new Steinmetz quip or action being delightedly passed around the student body.

"Did you hear what Steiny did last night? He smoked in the faculty meeting and President Raymond didn't have the courage to say anything. Oh, man!"

And again:

"Did you hear what Steiny said in his class today? Some guy asked if it was true that lightning never struck in the same place twice, and Steiny said yes, it was true. Then the guy asked why, and Steiny said because there was nothing there for lightning to strike the second time."

And:

"Did you hear about last night at the Van Curler Opera House? Big affair, you know, all the faculty had to go. Guess what Steiny did. Showed up in his turtleneck sweater and tweed jacket. Wow! Who'd ever dare do that but Steiny?"

Steinmetz was far and away the most popular man ever to have joined the faculty and the students devised many ways of displaying their regard and affection. One day after class a committee of four called upon the little professor. At first he thought they desired some assistance with their studies but then he saw that none of them was an engineering student. Also, there was a solemnity about them that indicated their mission related to something more important than their studies.

Steinmetz gave a little bow and said, "Gentlemen."

"Professor Steinmetz," the spokesman said, "we are the pledge committee of the Phi Gamma Delta fraternity."

"Ah yes, quite so."

"We would like you to join our fraternity, sir."

Steinmetz looked up in quick surprise, wondering if he had heard correctly. "You ... you want *me* to pledge Phi Gam?"

"Oh no, sir, not pledge. We held a special meeting and voted you in."

For several moments the little man was speechless, for he knew the import of this. No faculty member ever became a member of a fraternity unless he had joined in his undergraduate days. There were faculty *advisors* of fraternities, of course, but he was not being asked for that. He was being asked to join on the full and serious equality of an undergraduate.

At last he said, "There was no opposition . . . no black-ball?" The question was half in jest, but through it peeked his old feeling of inferiority, his fear of ridicule.

"The vote was unanimous, sir. We have been instructed to call upon you and ask you to become a brother."

"A brother," he murmured. He removed his glasses and polished them, he looked at the ceiling, he studied the floor. When he was at last able to speak in a controlled voice, he said, "I am honored. I accept your invitation."

Brother Steiny, as he became known to all Phi Gams, was inducted into the fraternity by grave and secret ritual and henceforth became one of the most active members of the house. He seldom missed a meeting, either social or business, and during the more outlandish hijinks he would sit quietly with his cigar, a gentle smile of nostalgia on his face. Breslau and Schenectady were not too different after all.

In true fraternity spirit he considered his bonds to his "brothers" paramount to those of the school and he master-minded several skirmishes between the Phi Gams and the administration. After a fund-raising campaign the fraternity eyed some choice campus land on which to build its new house. But Steinmetz knew that the college policy was to keep fraternities off the campus.

He rose in meeting and said, "Brothers, I suggest that

we demand the lot right next to President Raymond's house. This is in the middle of the campus and will bring cries of outrage from the administration. They'll never let us have it, of course."

"Then why ask for it, Brother Steiny?"

He smiled slyly and said, "For purposes of bargaining. We'll stand firm for a while, then, with all reasonableness, will agree to arbitrate the issue, and will eventually settle for the land we've wanted all along."

There were cries of delight as the strategy was endorsed. It worked just as Steinmetz had predicted.

Criticism came Steinmetz's way because of his fraternity activities and he felt impelled to write a serious treatise titled "The Purpose and Meaning of College Fraternities." It was a semi-sociological tract about the right of man to organize into societies for the creation of greater influence toward the achievement of specific goals. What he was too shy to write about was the truth of his own experience—the wonderful fact that he had come to college without brothers and now suddenly he had them.

CHAPTER ELEVEN

MEN WHO ACHIEVE eminence in one field are often considered by the public to be authorities in a great many other areas entirely unrelated to their specialty. And, quite humanly, such men often consider the public correct. Steinmetz was deluged by correspondence and visitors seeking his views on issues and problems far removed from mathematics and electricity, and he gave each inquiry careful, sober attention.

In one week's time he informed Edison on the property of insulators that would withstand high voltage (this *was* in his field), gave Henry Ford his views on the rehabilitation of criminals, advised a dean of Columbia University on the proper courses in history, criticized fire-prevention methods, opposed electricity as a "humane" way of killing animals, lectured opthalmologists on eyesight, denounced politicians for graft, opposed the diverting of mountain lands and streams to any but public use, declared that war was an "insanity," advised a young man on the selection of a publisher for his book, endorsed two young scientists for admission to the American Institute of Electrical Engineers, endorsed an educator for the presidency of a Midwestern college, revealed his favorite cooking recipe for camping life, entered into an extensive correspondence with a tropical-fish importer as he ordered twenty-two varieties for his aquarium and ended the letter with the stern admonition, "Send me only those fish who live together happily without eating each other."

And through all this he continued his research into all phases of electrical engineering. He had by now a total of 195 patents in his name, forty of them relating to alternating current and its distribution. The mountain of work that he undertook was never allowed to come between him and an inquiring mind of another man. Engineers and students, in particular, could always find cheerful help when they went to Steinmetz. Charles Wood, a newspaperman, told of one such visit:

Dr. Steinmetz had worked himself to the very top of the electrical engineering profession when I first came in contact with him. It was not as a newspaperman that I first met him. I was brought to his laboratory by a machinist who wanted to ask him a question about mechanical principles which were too deep for a mere newspaperman to understand.

I ventured a few questions about the schools of Schenectady and was surprised at the simple way he answered me. I discovered that I had been afraid of him; I was afraid of his knowledge, afraid of the big head which had solved a thousand mysteries and which must look with contempt, I thought, at the rank and file of cheerful idiots about him. I said something, in fact, concerning a hope that he would not consider my questions foolish.

"There are no foolish questions," he said, with an engaging grin. "No man really becomes a fool until he stops asking questions. The science of education is the science of helping people find out what they want to know."

Which is one of the reasons why I call Charles Steinmetz the greatest man I ever met. He was so much more than a specialist, although he was so much of a specialist he wrote textbooks which only the most highly trained specialists in his particular line could read. Yet he denied he was a "wizard" and had no desire to play the role. What he had learned about electricity, he pointed out, was due to his being curious about it. He simply asked questions, and one question led to another, and there he was.

His family and associates tried to shield him from public intrusion but it was almost impossible because he so enjoyed meeting people. No man presented himself at Steinmetz's door, whether for a handout or advice, without receiving what he asked for. However, he finally had to admit it was interfering with his work.

"Mousie," he said to his daughter-in-law, "I've got to get away from all these interruptions."

She spread her hands. "We try to keep people out but...."

"I know, I know. It's my fault. But I have a solution to it. I'm going to build a cabin on the creek."

Some years before Steinmetz had acquired several acres of land on Viele's Creek that fed into the Mohawk River northwest of Schenectady. Here was where he and his cronies picnicked and camped and swam.

"I'll be completely isolated out there," he continued excitedly. "I won't even put in a telephone. I can get an enormous amount of work done."

"I think it's a wonderful idea," Mousie said.

"I'll get some carpenters right at it and it should be done in time for the children and me to spend the summer there."

"The children! You don't plan on taking *them* with you!"

"Oh, of course. There's so much for them to learn out there in the woods—nature lore and wild life. And they can learn to swim in the creek. It will be good for them. And I'll take good care of them, Mousie, you don't have to worry."

"But the whole idea is for you to work without interruptions!"

"The children don't interrupt me."

This was such a patent lie that the two of them broke into laughter. Mousie had done her level best to keep the children out of their grandfather's laboratory during his working hours, but had been thwarted at every turn. Steinmetz always put his work down cheerfully at the first appearance of a grandchild. Sometimes they would even bring friends and ask him to demonstrate various pieces of equipment or settle a dispute or even tell them a story. He never failed them.

The laboratory itself was a great attraction and the children would bend glass tubes over Bunsen burners, mix chemicals in the soapstone sinks, use the imported cypress lumber (intended for test-tube racks) to make model boats, weigh toys on the delicate scales under the glass dome, handle his fragile beakers and Erlenmeyer flasks. Steinmetz watched it all benignly, happily, requiring only that they not touch the equipment he was using at the moment, and that they clean up after themselves.

Nor did he have privacy in his office, for here were the glass cases that held his fascinating collections of butterflies, rocks, Indian tools, ostrich eggs, gourds, bottles of dead lizards, stuffed animals, and a shrunken head. It was a museum that was ever growing, for now the grand-children brought their own treasures to it, and no matter what they were, Steinmetz labeled them with small museum cards and put them on display. Joe brought a rusty nail and it was duly displayed with the legend "Nail dug up by Joe at Ft. Ticonderoga."

Only once did Steinmetz run out of patience. One Saturday morning Joe had interrupted his grandfather in the office four times. The fifth time Steinmetz sighed heavily, got up from his desk and went to one of the glass display cases, where he slowly and elaborately removed the exhibits. Then he put Joe inside the case and took a picture of him. When developed and printed, this picture was placed in the museum with the caption "Great archeological find made by Charles P. Steinmetz . . . a rare specimen . . . never another like it in the history of the world."

Steinmetz's claim that the children didn't really bother him was probably true. He had such remarkable powers of concentration that he could easily come out of a problem and move back into it without the loss of any of the premises. But the mother not only found this difficult to believe; she was also naturally annoyed at the conspiracy against her orders.

She said sternly, "Not less than an hour ago I saw Joe go into the lab when you were working. And I had specifically told him. . . ."

"I know, but it was important, Mousie."

"What was so important?"

"He's considering going into the stamp business."

"He had to interrupt you with that?"

"Yes, of course. He had to catch the next mail with his first wholesale order."

"You don't have to tell me the rest, Daddy. You gave him the money to buy the stamps."

"It was a good business proposition. When he has those stamps for sale I'm sure to need some of them for my own collection."

Mousie sighed and shook her head in frustration and defeat.

The camp at Viele's Creek was not completed all at once. Each year saw new wings added until finally it was a gerrymandered structure of open studs and pine siding with a central living room that contained a cot for Steinmetz, the kitchen and dining room in the left wing and on the right a dormitory bedroom large enough to contain the grandchildren plus their visiting friends.

Camp Mohawk, as it was named, provided a series of long, idyllic summers for Steinmetz and his grand-children. The shallow stream was dammed up to provide a small lake with an island in the middle of it, and on these waters the family swam and canoed, and around the shoreline they took long walks to study the birds and plant life.

The daily routine was flexible but generally the same. Each morning Steinmetz rose with the dawn, put on his bathing suit, and then stood in the doorway of the dormi-tory to bang on a kettle with a wooden spoon and cry out, "Everybody up for cuddle-muddle! Everybody up for cuddle-muddle."

Cuddle-muddle was whatever he happened to be cook-ing, usually a cross between stew and hash, prepared in a battered old pan over a kerosene flame. He stirred the gooey mixture with the gestures of a French chef and each day would announce the dish was even better than the day before. This steady diet soon palled on adult visitors, but the children thrived on it.

After breakfast and clean-up, a cursory operation, Steinmetz retired to his "office," a contraption designed to solve a number of his problems and frustrations. He loved to be near the water but he couldn't swim; he wanted a vacation but he couldn't stop working. So he bought a canoe and placed a wide plank athwart the gunwale. On the plank was a box of sharp pencils, a pad of paper, a book of logarithms, and a tin can of cigars. He knelt in the middle of the canoe and leaned over the board to work as he floated up- and downstream. Occasionally he would employ a double-bladed paddle to propel himself into a cove to study a bird or wildflower.

Afternoons were given over to play with the children and to the promotion of various contests among them and with the lab boys who came out to assist him with his work. He kept a diary of his days at Camp Mohawk. One entry read:

Yesterday Felix [a lab boy] paddled around the island in 19 min. I told him that Emil [another lab boy] had a record of 13 min. Thus he tried again after supper and got around in 17 min. He spent most of today looking up Emil's record in the diary; finally found it, but it was 23 min. and the 13 min. was a mistake. Sorry he found it, otherwise he would continue to try to beat 13 min.

One July Fourth entry read:

Billy and Midget went with Felix for fireworks on Friday and got some; Felix brought them out yesterday and Billy tried them by setting off by a hammerblow one of those things which make racket when you step on. It went off OK and Billy has some *yellow fingers on the left hand, from $C_6H_2OH(NO_2)_3$, and knows more.*

Nighttime was still story-telling time. Steinmetz had brought the *Book of Knowledge* to camp and often read aloud from it, but his own stories were even better. When he told what made the stars twinkle and the wind blow, he spoke sound science but with such imagery that the children were spellbound. There came a time, however, when he decided that the children were old enough to receive some sterner fare. On a stormy night he launched into the telling of "Dracula." What moans of delicious terror! What cruel dilemmas between wanting to hear more and not daring to!

The story was such a success that Steinmetz had to tell it night after night, improvising as he went along. There were young guests for the night during one of the tellings, and in the middle of the tale eight-year-old Edgar, a friend of Billy's, got out of bed and edged toward the door.

"Where are you going?" Steinmetz asked.

"I . . . I'm gonna get into a canoe and go to the island. I'm gonna stay all night on the island."

"But why, Edgar?"

"Vampires can't fly over running water. You said so yourself."

With some difficulty the guest was reinstalled in bed, but that was not the end of it. Upon returning home Edgar revealed the camp story to his mother, who in turn made a call upon Mrs. Hayden. And Mousie closed the circle by going out to camp for a discussion with Steinmetz.

"Daddy," she said sternly, "what kind of stories have you been telling the children?"

Steinmetz dissembled, though a poor and obvious thing it was. He frowned thoughtfully, pulled at his beard, finally said, "Well, Mousie, I've been reading to them from the *Book of Knowledge*."

"That's not what I mean, and you know it."

"No?" he said, wide-eyed with spurious innocence.

"You've been telling them blood-curdling stories about bats and vampires and all sorts of terrible things."

"Oh, that," he said dismissively.

"Yes, that! Edgar's mother tells me he had nightmares for a week after hearing your stories. Now, Daddy, you just have to stop scaring the children."

He nodded in ready agreement. "I guess Edgar is a bit delicate for Dracula. I won't tell it again when he's around."

"It's not just Edgar. I don't want you to tell those stories to Joe and Midge and Billy."

"*They* don't get nightmares."

"Nevertheless I don't want them exposed to such things. Now you must promise me."

Meekly, "All right, Mousie."

That night, when Steinmetz and his grandchildren were again alone, the call came from the bedroom, "Daddy, tell us a story."

He sighed, picked up a volume of the *Book of Knowledge*, and entered the bedroom to find three eager young faces peering from behind the sheets. At the sight of the book, however, their faces fell.

"We want to hear about Dracula," they chorused.

"Mousie says those stories scare you too much."

"They do not," Billy cried. "I don't get scared, hardly at all."

"Edgar did," Steinmetz said.

They giggled. "He wanted to sleep on the island," Midge said.

"We shouldn't scare Edgar," Steinmetz said.

"But he's not here," Joe exclaimed. "He's all the way back in Schenectady."

"I know, I know," said Steinmetz, "but sometimes the stories ride through the night winds. Sometimes, no matter how softly you speak, your words are snatched up and carried off to scare someone who is miles and miles away."

Midge sat straight up in bed, her face bright with excitement. She said, "Let's scare Edgar."

"Yes . . . yes," chorused her brothers. "Tell the story, Daddy, and scare Edgar."

Steinmetz dropped his voice to a whisper. "You mustn't tell Mousie."

"Noooo!" they whispered back.

He put down the *Book of Knowledge* and pulled up a chair. Henceforth, the secret code between them all was "Let's scare Edgar."

CHAPTER TWELVE

STEINMETZ LOST his temper publicly only once in his life. In 1911 the citizens of Schenectady elected a reform candidate for mayor, a Protestant minister and Socialist by the name of George R. Lunn. Remembering his idealistic youth, his flight from Bismarck because of his socialistic principles, Steinmetz wanted to make some gesture of support to the new administration, and he wrote a letter to the mayor offering his services in any capacity. Lunn wisely appointed the town's most famous citizen to the Board of Education. The move was a popular one, for Steinmetz was an educator, after all, and the Schenectady school system was shockingly behind the times.

At the first meeting of the Board, Steinmetz was elected president, and he immediately presented a long-range program for the rehabilitation of the schools. Construction of new schools was the first and most pressing need, and Steinmetz had designed a building that was ahead of its time and was to be generally adopted by school architects forty years later. His sketch revealed a rectangular, boxlike two-story building. He explained that to build it higher was unsafe and to build it lower was uneconomical use of the land. These were to be self-contained units with all services and classrooms, and could be added to existing buildings without additional architects' fees.

Each school was to have a large play yard and extensive recreational facilities available to the neighborhood the year round. He proposed open-air schools for the tubercular, ungraded schools for the retarded, a permanent health program with a staff of nurses and doctors, and increased pay for the teaching staff.

This was exactly what the reform forces had hoped Steinmetz would do and they hailed his program as one destined to place Schenectady schools among the best in the nation. But they hailed it too quickly and without remembering that the old-line politicians controlled the purse strings through the Board of Estimate and Apportionment. This Board heard Steinmetz's proposals with patient boredom and then appropriated just sufficient money to run the antiquated school system exactly as it was.

Steinmetz was completely mystified by his defeat. He said to his son that night, "I don't understand it, Roy. I just can't follow their reasoning."

"I think it's simple enough," Hayden said. "What you propose costs money and they don't want to spend it."

"But our children's future is at stake!" Steinmetz cried. "That is what I can't understand . . . those men's indifference to the children."

"They're not entirely indifferent, I shouldn't imagine, it's just that they think primarily about votes. They're afraid that spending a lot of money will prove unpopular and mean defeat for them in the next election. After all, they're politicians. I don't think you can lick the politicians."

"Oh, I don't know," said Steinmetz, and grinned. "I may become a politician myself."

Two years later he announced his candidacy for president of the Schenectady Common Council. His family and friends were appalled, for they feared his health was not robust enough for the wear and tear of politics. The civic leaders who supported his school program were dismayed for a different reason. Their logic told them he was the poorest possible candidate for elective office; he was frail and deformed, his voice was high-pitched and his speech thickened by a German accent. What kind of a platform appearance would he make? A disastrous one, surely! And added to all these handicaps, Steinmetz refused to disavow his socialistic principles. Socialism, even the mild and humanitarian brand he held, was not popular in America and there were certain to be bitter and scurrilous attacks upon him. His close friends urged him to think of himself. He was now a successful and honored man and they begged him not to subject himself to the erosion of politics.

He thought about it, as he was urged, but there could be only one conclusion. The President of the Common Council automatically had a seat and a vote in the Board of Estimate, and it was the Board of Estimate who appropriated money for the schools. The welfare of the children came before his own ease, and he went through with the campaign.

He was elected overwhelmingly.

On the Board of Estimate he tirelessly lectured, goaded, instructed, and finally inspired the politicians to make sufficient funds available for a modern school system.

During his term, eight new schools were built, special classes were created for retarded children, a corps of school nurses established, and a network of school playgrounds constructed. Steinmetz became the father of the modern Schenectady school system and he took as much pride in his accomplishments here as in those reached in the laboratory.

Not everyone in Schenectady shared Steinmetz's pride in the new school system; there were at least two strong dissenters, as he was to learn.

It was on a clear fall day when he had gone out to camp for a week end of work with his lab boy, Emil Remscheid. Steinmetz spent the morning drifting and working in his canoe, and had just come in for lunch when he heard sounds of approaching visitors. The path leading down to the cabin was a steep one, and falling pebbles always arrived to bang against the back door before the caller was in sight.

"Someone is coming, Doctor," Remscheid announced unnecessarily.

Steinmetz sighed. "Go see who it is, Emil."

The young man disappeared, there was a murmur of voices at the back door, and then he returned with two formidable grim-visaged matrons. Steinmetz rose to his feet, gave a small bow, and said, "Ladies."

They towered over him and looked down with hostile eyes. The larger of the two said, "You are Doctor Steinmetz, the President of the School Board?"

"Yes."

"Then you must be responsible for what is going on."

He smiled quizzically. "I dare say I am."

"Sir, we refer to a violation of citizens' rights, to a public nuisance, to the outrageous invasion of a peaceful neighborhood because of *you!* We demand that something be done!"

Steinmetz pulled at his whiskers. "Won't you sit down, ladies?"

They would not sit down, and told their story with self-righteous indignation. These two ladies lived in a house next to a newly constructed school play yard. Not only did the voices of the children disturb them, but one of the boys had recently retrieved a ball off their lawn and stepped on a peony bush.

Steinmetz listened at first in disbelief, and then in shock. His face was quite pale when they finally ran out of words, and he asked with deceptive calmness, "What do you ladies propose that I do? Should I lock the children in the school building and deny them exercise and fresh air?"

"We don't care what you do so long as you keep the little monsters from disturbing decent citizens."

"You consider yourself decent citizens?" Steinmetz demanded, his voice cracking under the pressure of his mounting anger.

"Do you dare to say that we are not?"

"I dare to say a good deal about you, Madam," Steinmetz cried in a shrill voice. Then he laced into them, lectured them, denounced them, waving his fist angrily as he shouted. Thinking they had come to grips with a madman, the ladies retreated step by step toward the back door, and Steinmetz followed them, his chin thrust forward, his eyes blazing.

The ladies left in disorder, tumbling over each other to get out the door and up the steep path to safety. After they had gone, Steinmetz began to tremble and had to sit down.

"You all right, Doctor?" Remscheid asked, hovering over him.

Steinmetz drank half a glass of water, put it down and sighed. "I'm all right, Emil. I guess I must have lost my temper."

"You sure did," the boy said admiringly. "You sure told them off."

"Quite an experience, losing your temper," the little man said. "Blood pressure goes up, no doubt. Respiration increases, vision blurs a little. Quite an experience." He laughed. "I guess it's good for a man to lose his temper once in a lifetime . . . then you know what it's like."

CHAPTER THIRTEEN

INEVITABLY CAMP MOHAWK BECAME less and less a vacation retreat and more and more a summer workshop. Steinmetz's deep immersion in his work could not be entirely set aside even for the lures of nature, and so he performed miracles of electrical calculations while floating in his canoe. And, though he held out against the installation of a telephone, his privacy was increasingly violated by people both important and unimportant. The world was quite literally beating a path to his door.

One morning a junior executive from G.E. appeared in camp to announce excitedly that some foreign dignitaries were in Schenectady and asking to meet Steinmetz. The American State Department had officially requested that their wishes be granted if at all possible.

"Do you think, Doctor Steinmetz, you could see them this afternoon?" the young man asked.

"Sure, sure. If they come out to camp, I'll talk to them."

"Thank you, sir. I'll bring them out this afternoon around three o'clock."

"Good," Steinmetz said, waving his hand as he bent his head over his canoe workboard.

That afternoon the dignitaries arrived, escorted not

only by the G.E. official but by a State Department protocol officer. All, except the G.E. man, were dressed in formal cutaways with striped pants, and silk top hats. As the elegantly dressed men began to negotiate the steep path their spats caught in brambles, their hats were knocked off by overhanging branches and their equanimity perilously upset.

Moreover, when they finally arrived at the cabin, no one was there to receive them. The G.E. man, face aflame with embarrassment, saw Steinmetz still floating and working in his canoe. He hailed him ashore.

Steinmetz beached his canoe, called a greeting and, dressed in an old bathing suit, walked up to meet his distinguished guests. As he began to talk in quick, idiomatic French, the guests forgot his twisted body and were captivated by his charm and his quicksilver mind. When they left camp an hour later they confided to the State Department man that this meeting with Steinmetz was most certainly the highlight of their entire visit to America.

Steinmetz was popular not only with foreign dignitaries but with other scientists as well. His laboratory was visited by Marconi, Einstein, Edison, and Edison's one-time employee, Nikola Tesla. Tesla, too, was a naturalized citizen, and shared with Steinmetz reverence for his new homeland. He was a pioneer in high-tension electricity and designed some of the equipment employed to harness Niagara Falls for the production of hydroelectric power.

The well-known writer, editor, printer, and home-spun philosopher, Elbert Hubbard, became acquainted with Steinmetz and wrote, "Steinmetz, next to Edison, is our great modern mechanical prophet. Steinmetz seems possessed of faculties beyond those of the average man. He has an intuitional sense that is almost uncanny. His 'boys' may work on an electrical problem for a year or more and fail to make it tangible. Steinmetz will then sit down and look at the machine for about five minutes, light a cigar, blow a cloud of smoke through it, and behold, the thing starts and chaos becomes cosmos!"

The most welcome guests of all were, of course, the youth. Emil Remscheid, the combination lab boy and chauffeur, was at this time a college freshman and often brought his own friends to camp for week ends. Sometimes there would be as many as a half-dozen teen-agers present from Friday until Sunday night, and Steinmetz cooked great piles of wheatcakes for them, along with his now-famous (or infamous) cuddle-muddle.

He hated washing dishes, however, and often saved a week's supply to spring on the boys, saying, "As long as you're going to wash, you might as well make it worth while."

These teen-agers adored Steinmetz, not only because he was generous but because he treated them like adults. They could discuss any topic during the long week ends and never have the feeling they were being patronized by their host. And another great advantage during the fall was that Steinmetz was always happy to help them with their homework.

One young man had labored quietly but desperately over his books in a corner of the cabin porch until Steinmetz approached him almost diffidently and asked what the problem was. He was an engineering student and had a week-long assignment to figure some extremely complicated stresses on a bridge. The work had to be turned in Monday morning and he still hadn't solved it. Steinmetz read the problem and then, after a few rapid pencil calculations, gave him the answer.

The following week end the boy returned to camp and there was new awe in his eyes as he looked at his host. "Gee, Doctor Steinmetz, do you know what happened in class last Monday? Remember the stress problem?"

"I remember."

"Well, the professor asked who had solved it and not a single guy had been able to come up with the answer. When I found that out, *I* sure wasn't going to claim to have solved it. But after class I took your answer to the professor and told him about it. He looked at your figures and could hardly believe it. He had to use the entire blackboard to work it out, but you had done it in only *two* mathematical equations! Golly, sir!"

It was in Emil Remscheid's presence that Steinmetz made his most spectacular electrical discovery, one for which the world press dubbed him "The Modern Jove."

The nation's power industry, employing the alternating current in which Steinmetz was so interested, now had many thousands of miles of high-tension lines stretching across the country. However, there was an implacable enemy that struck without warning and caused great damage—lightning. This phenomenon of nature would melt power lines, burn out transformers, and in some instances even travel back to the generators to melt vital parts. Because of lightning damage it was impossible to maintain the steady and constant supply of power needed by industry if it was to grow. Every storm meant a breakdown in current supply somewhere in the nation and it was sometimes a matter of weeks before sufficient repairs could be made to resume service.

Steinmetz plunged himself into this, determined to evolve a way for the power systems to absorb harmlessly the tremendous thrust of electricity from a thunderbolt. But the great handicap he faced was nature's reluctance to cooperate in his research; the lightning never struck when he was present.

North of Schenectady was a hill scarred by lightning over the years, and one summer Steinmetz had a tower erected there and attached to the tower all sorts of meters and other instruments. He manned the tower around the clock with scientists, to read the meters and interpret the instruments. Lightning never came near the hill all summer long.

In a press interview Steinmetz explained the problem in these terms: "The difference between lightning and ordinary current is similar to that between a pound of dynamite and a pint of gasoline; the pint of gasoline contains more energy and can do more work than the pound of dynamite, but the pint of gasoline gives off its energy only slowly, at a moderate rate of power, while the pound of dynamite gives off its energy explosively, all at once, at an enormous rate of power, and thereby locally tears and destroys."

This interview revealed again Steinmetz's great talent for being able to simplify for the layman a very complex concept, but that simplification did not help him reach the solution to the problem. But nature suddenly and unexpectedly did cooperate and Steinmetz was off to another of his brilliant successes.

It was in the springtime when great, dark clouds rolled up the Mohawk Valley to bring rain to the fresh-planted earth, and to accompany this largess with angry thunder and the savagery of lightning. On Friday afternoon young Emil Remscheid was to drive Steinmetz out to camp for the week end, but when a torrential storm broke over Schenectady the trip was delayed until the following day. On a sunny Saturday morning the electric car moved at a stately pace out of the Wendell Avenue driveway and headed for Camp Mohawk.

Upon arrival at Viele's Creek Remscheid parked the car and ran on ahead to open up the cabin. Steinmetz came more slowly down the steep path. When he arrived at camp the young man, white-faced, met him at the door.

"My gosh, Doctor," he exclaimed, "vandals have been here and wrecked everything."

Within the cabin there was indeed the senseless pattern of destruction which comes from vandals. The front-porch window on the right-hand side had been broken, apparently to permit entry. Steinmetz's worktable beside it had been upended and split in half. The electric wires that traveled the ceiling beams on white insulators had been cut in a dozen places. In the kitchen the zinc-lined icebox had been thrown on its side and its legs shattered, and in the opposite wing of the cabin, in the dormitory bedroom, a large mirror that hung on the back wall had been broken and scattered over the floor.

Steinmetz stepped into the cabin, took one look around

and cried excitedly, "We've had a visitor, Emil, but it was lightning! Lightning!" He danced from room to room, crying as he went, "Wonderful . . . oh, this is wonderful! That the lightning should have chosen our camp . . . how lucky we are! Oh . . . wonderful!"

At the end of the tour he turned to Emil and ordered, "Take the electric and go back to town and get the camera. I want to photograph every detail. Now hurry, my boy . . . top speed! This is a great day for us and we mustn't waste a moment of it."

By the time Emil had returned with the camera, Steinmetz had been able to reconstruct the event. A bolt of lightning had struck the tall tree just outside the front porch by Steinmetz's worktable. It traveled down the tree, shattered the window to hit the metal lamp on the table. Traveling through the wiring system, melting the wires as it went, it discharged on the zinc icebox in one wing, and in the other wing entered a long outside extension cord that was draped along the building behind the dormitory. The cord was hung on a wooden peg, wound in a dozen loops, and when the lightning got to this point the loops acted as a condenser to increase the voltage many times and finally discharge it through the side of the cabin and onto the silvered back of the mirror within.

Steinmetz stood at the door of the dormitory and looked down almost lovingly at the mess of scattered glass. "Emil, that mirror is our most important clue. Don't come in here until I finish putting it back together."

For the rest of that week end Steinmetz was on hands and knees to search out the tiniest slivers of glass and me-

ticulously put them back together like a great jigsaw puzzle. When at last it was done, he placed the reconstructed
mirror between two large plates of clear glass and sealed
the edges with tape. On the silvered back was burned the
bold pattern of the bolt.

"Look here, Emil! The picture of a bolt of lightning.
See where it struck? And see the melted ribbons where
it ran to the edges. We will now be able to calculate the
potential of lightning by measuring the distance from the
point of impact to the end of the melted streamers. Load
this in the car and let's get back to the laboratory and to
work!"

Things now began to happen in the fifth-floor Steinmetz laboratory at General Electric's Building 28. Men
and materials converged to create a strange-looking apparatus, only to tear it down; to calculate endlessly on sheets
of white paper, only to throw them in the wastebasket.
Something big was afoot—the entire city was aware of it
—but exactly what it was, no one seemed to know. The
scientists assigned to Steinmetz were given research projects in a variety of directions without any clear indication
of the end goals. Even Steinmetz himself did not really
seem to know; he was searching, searching. And all this
elaborate, complicated, expensive quest originated from
the most prosaic of objects, a shattered mirror.

At an ever-accelerating pace the research continued for
weeks into months and months into a year. Steinmetz
drove himself, spending all day and most of every night
at the laboratory. Whenever the search was blocked in
one avenue, he turned to another. He could not, would

not, conceive of defeat. Finally the city learned what he was up to; word seeped out that he was trying to *create* lightning! He was determined to produce it at will, and to control it, to direct it against whatever object he chose!

The city reacted variously to this news. The fundamentalist preachers cried from their pulpits that the creation of lightning was God's province and woe to the man who presumed to encroach upon it. The city fathers wondered if Steinmetz was not creating a terrible hazard to life and property. Other men, some of them scientists, questioned the usefulness of man-made lightning. But no one entertained a doubt that Steinmetz would do what he planned to do. He was a genius, they all agreed, wicked or wise depending on one's point of view, but undeniably a genius.

In the winter of 1922 there came from Steinmetz's laboratory a series of violent explosions. At first the town thought the little man had blown himself up, but he appeared smiling and unhurt to announce a press conference and demonstration in his laboratory for the following week.

On the appointed day the newspaper reporters and photographers and high company officials were admitted to the laboratory to find a monstrous strange machine—a lightning machine! It towered two stories high, carrying rack on rack of large glass plates covered with foil. These were to serve as condensers to build the electrical energy to extremely high current. The source of energy was from the local power system. The voltage of the local system was stepped up through high-voltage transformers, then rectified through glass vacuum tubes known as "kenotrons" which in turn charged the glass-plate condensers. Two ominous-looking brass domes, called "sphere gaps," were to carry the bolt of lightning when it exploded. The plan was to turn the current loose in the condensers and let it build and build in power and force until all the condensers would discharge simultaneously.

The press and notables, including Thomas Edison, stood behind a protective wire screen to view the machine with awe and speculation. The hum of conversation suddenly ceased for into the room came the machine's master —Steinmetz.

"Good morning, good morning," he said briskly to the crowd, then conferred in low tones with his associates. When he was satisfied that all was ready, he turned to the row of newspaper photographers to ask how they proposed to record the lightning on their photographic plates. They told him in some detail and when they had finished, he suggested that they alter their lens openings and shutter speeds. Immediately every professional photographer set his camera exactly to Steinmetz's figures.

There was an additional bit of drama now introduced. A model village, complete with church steeple and tree-lined streets, was placed between the sphere gaps. It was to be struck by lightning!

At last everything was ready and a hush fell on the assembly. Steinmetz gave a small nod of his head and an assistant threw a switch. All was silent—— No, there was a small hum as the condensers began to gather their charge of electricity. The hum grew no louder except in the tense imagination of the spectators. Some of them apprehensively placed their hands over their ears; all braced themselves.

Then it came—a blazing flash of lightning, followed by a thunderous crash of sound that shook the room. The air filled with dust and a sulphurous odor. As soon as the reporters recovered their breath they looked for the model village. It was gone . . . vanished . . . atomized!

Steinmetz began speaking in a matter-of-fact voice. "The characteristic of lightning is high voltage, backed by very large power, lasting for a very short time only, and so giving explosive effects. In certain of the high-frequency experiments of Professor Thomson, Tesla, and others, the voltage is very high but with little power back of it. In our lightning generator we get a discharge of ten thousand amperes, at over a hundred thousand volts; that is, a power of over a million horsepower, lasting for a hundred-thousandth of a second. This gives us the explosive, tearing and shattering effects of real lightning."

That night the newspapers around the world carried big headlines reading, MODERN JOVE SITS ON THRONE AND HURLS THUNDERBOLTS AT WILL.

Now that Steinmetz could create lightning at will, he could use it to build and test lightning-proof generators and transformers and transmission wires. He soon developed the lightning arrester, the sentinel of the whole power system, the guardian of the powerhouse. It operated with a swiftness equaled only by lightning itself.

What it did was to automatically open a path by which the vast voltage of a lightning bolt could jump harmlessly to the ground instead of entering the power system and melting the equipment. It was as simple as that, but as in many simple things, a genius was required to conceive it.

Steinmetz, who had done so much to help make possible nationwide electrification in the first place, had now succeeded in protecting it against the power caprice of nature. A sinew of America's coming industrial greatness had been created.

CHAPTER FOURTEEN

AFTER THE TWO YEARS of concentrated work on lightning, Steinmetz was tired, dry of ideas, and he sought refreshment, as always, in his grandchildren. But now a subtle change had taken place in their relationship. As small children their love had been uncomplicated. It had been in response to his own love and in gratitude for the fun he gave them. Now they were in their teens and no longer saw life only through the prism of self; they had achieved a degree of objectivity along with a new kind of imagination—the ability to feel another's pain.

Joe, seventeen, Midge, fourteen, and Billy, twelve, looked at their grandfather and realized he was both larger and smaller than they had once thought. They now knew the extent of his wisdom and his fame and this made them proud and possessive; they also saw he was a frail little hunchback and this made them protective.

Steinmetz had always been absent-minded in regard to the mechanics of living, but now the children began to cope with it, perhaps even exaggerating it. It was Joe's job to wake his grandfather each morning and he'd go into the large front bedroom, close the window, then gently shake the tiny figure in the large bed. "Daddy, it's time to get up. Hey, Daddy, it's time."

119

"Okay . . . okay," Steinmetz would say, immediately awake and bright and cheerful.

Joe would pick up the clothes dropped in a pile, the pants and the underwear and the turtleneck sweater, and drape them over the back of the chair. "Here are your clothes, Daddy." As if the little man could not find them without help.

When Steinmetz came down to breakfast all the children quickly inspected him to find anything wrong. Midge was usually the quickest, and she'd cry out in motherly exasperation, "Daddy! You forgot to tie your shoelaces. You'll trip and fall if you go around like that." Then she'd run and tie them for him while he stood there with a sheepish and pleased smile.

If it was raining out and he started toward the front door, the children would cry in chorus, "Daddy! You're forgetting your rubbers."

"My goodness, so I was!" he'd reply with happy scorn of himself.

The parties had changed, too. No longer did his grandchildren and their friends demand that he do magic tricks and create fireworks; he was not the center of attention he had once been. But he didn't mind as long as he was merely present. He hired small dance orchestras and watched happily while boys and girls who had once squealed with delight at hot lead being dropped into a bucket of water now waltzed and one-stepped with adolescent dignity.

He continued to spoil the children with gifts which grew larger and more expensive by the year. When Joe was about to go away to a preparatory school, his grandfather took him aside and said, "Now you must be certain to write home to the family once a week. And if there is anything private you want to say to me in the letter, say it in the Morse code I taught you at camp last summer."

Quite frequently Joe had private things to say to his grandfather and Mousie complained strongly about the code. She was positive her son was asking for extra spending money, but of course she couldn't prove it because Steinmetz refused to teach her the code.

It was Midge who discovered that there was one thing none of them could do for Steinmetz: they could not protect him from his own secret hurt. She learned this one afternoon when the two of them took a walk together and wandered off into a slum area of the city. Steinmetz was not a familiar figure in these squalid blocks, and the people who spent all their waking hours in a fierce struggle for life's essentials could not know or care for another man's renown.

These two aliens walked along, deep in conversation and oblivious to their surroundings. The girl walked with coltish grace; the man, a head shorter, hitched himself rapidly along on his spindly legs, a motion that strangely did not detract from his dignity.

Then suddenly a mocking laugh brought them out of themselves. Midge looked across the street in the direction of the sound and saw a cluster of slum-cruel boys. With mounting horror she saw they were pretending to be hunchbacked! They limped, they staggered, they clawed the air and gave out gutteral cries.

"I'm d' missin' link! I'm d' missin' link!" one of them shouted over and over, capering monkeylike.

It was unreal, a nightmare. She glanced quickly at her grandfather but he was looking straight ahead, his face expressionless.

"I'm d' missin' link!" came the shrill, taunting voice.

She paused, not knowing what to do, whether to fly at the tormentors or to scream back at them, but unable to endure things as they were. A hand took her firmly by the arm and moved her forward again. Her grandfather's hand was neither commanding nor pleading; it was a comradely grip that said *We were out for a walk, weren't we? Well, then, let's walk.*

He neither hastened his steps nor slowed them, and he resumed the conversation that had been briefly interrupted. She had often wondered if he faced this sort of thing, wondered how he would handle it. She had not guessed he would be so calm and brave. Tears stung her eyes, tears of love and pride and anger.

"I'm d' missin' link," came the implacable voice.

"Oh, you—you——" chokingly she called the boy a name Steinmetz had never heard her use.

Soon they were in the business district and their tormentors dropped away. No reference was made to their experience when they arrived home, and she didn't even tell her brothers about it. It was a precious sort of pain and she didn't want to share it. It made her love her grandfather in a way she never had before.

Two days later when they were alone together in the greenhouse, her grandfather said, "Midgie, you must never call anyone that kind of name."

She was startled, for she had no idea she'd said the word aloud.

He continued, "You must never call anyone a name that means their race or nationality is not as good as any other. Those are cruel words. And they're untrue words. There is goodness in all men and we must respect that goodness even if we can't see it at the moment." He smiled at her. "Okay?"

She grinned back. "Okay."

The American Institute of Electrical Engineers was to hold its annual convention in Del Monte, California, in October, 1923, and invited the nation's most famous scientist to address it.

"What do you think, Mousie?" Steinmetz asked his daughter. "Should we go?"

"We?"

"I wouldn't want to go without the family. It would be a chance to see the country. We'll make it a big vacation."

"The children will be in school, Daddy."

He dismissed that objection with a wave of the hand. "The Great Plains, the Rockies, the deserts, Grand Canyon, Hollywood . . . we'll do the works. That will be educational, don't you think so? Come on, Mousie, let's do it!"

She sighed and said, "If I know you, you've already told the children and I'm outvoted."

The trip west, made by Pullman, turned out to be a triumphal tour. Crowds appeared at every stop to gaze at the "wizard," and invitations to speak began pouring in from every city on the itinerary. Steinmetz accepted several, the first one in Denver, and the auditoriums were always packed. William Jennings Byran joined his train to discuss religion; mayors and governors jostled each other to be photographed with the "Modern Jove," and in Hollywood he was entertained by the reigning royalty, Douglas Fairbanks and Mary Pickford.

The men and women who came to hear him speak were aware that they were looking at one of the great men of their era and they wanted not only the memory of his presence but they hoped he might give them some wisdom they could apply to their own lives. Steinmetz did not disappoint them. More and more over the recent years he had been thinking and writing in philosophical terms. By now he was the author of thirteen books and more than sixty articles, only a small percentage of them dealing with electricity. He had thought deeply on life; he had suffered and he had triumphed, and acquired wisdom.

He had advice for the youth:

"If a young man goes at his work as a means of making money only, I am not interested in him. However, I am interested if he seems to do his work for work's sake, for the satisfaction he gets out of doing it. If I were to bequeath to every young man one virtue, I would give him the spirit of divine discontent, for without it the world would stand still. The man hard to satisfy moves forward. The man satisfied with what he has done moves backward."

Though he had been an agnostic, Steinmetz had by now achieved a greater wisdom, and he said, "Spiritual power is a force which history clearly teaches has been the greatest force in the development of men. Yet we have been merely playing with it and have never really studied it as we have the physical forces. Some day people will learn that material things do not bring happiness and are of little use in making people creative and powerful. Then the scientists of the world will turn their laboratories over to the study of spiritual forces which have hardly been scratched."

His speech before the engineering convention received a rousing ovation, a tribute from men whose careers had been largely created by him. On the way home he stopped off at Salt Lake City, where the Mormon Tabernacle Choir gave a special recital for him and his family.

On October 12 the train rolled out of the West and into familiar Schenectady, and within a half-hour he was home on Wendell Avenue. The "vacation" had lasted six weeks.

"Mousie, I'm tired," he said. Then, fearing that sounded like a complaint, he said, "The trip was worth while, I think. And certainly good for the children."

"It was a wonderful trip, Daddy," she said.

He nodded soberly, then gave her his sly smile. "Next year we'll take a cruise to the Mediterranean. Won't be so much walking."

Then he went to bed.

The next day he was still tired and a doctor was summoned. General exhaustion, the doctor said; nothing to be alarmed about, but he should stay in bed for a complete rest. Steinmetz grumbled but complied. On the morning of October 26, 1923, young Billy went to his grandfather's room with the breakfast tray to find him dead. His face was serene, without a trace of pain or worry. His heart had run down and stopped as easily as an electric motor deprived of current.   He was fifty-nine years old.

In his lifetime Steinmetz had had ample opportunity to accumulate riches but his estate was surprisingly small. He left a trust fund for his sister Clara, and to his adopted family went the Wendell Avenue house and a modest amount of cash.   Yet his legacy was great—it was to the world of science, to the users of electricity, to the students of Union College, to the neighborhood children who adored him, the lab boys who revered him, to the millions of ordinary people who had never met him but came to depend upon his gentle wisdom.

As news of his death flashed out, cablegrams of praise and sorrow poured into Schenectady from all over the world.   When his body was carried to the cemetery it was accompanied by the nation's leaders in science, industry, and government.   They had come to honor a man who had not only helped make America strong, but who was first among them in patience and generosity.

Steinmetz's entire life had been an avowal of love, and he was loved in return.   No man can earn a greater epitaph.

ABOUT THE AUTHOR

Floyd Miller has been a newspaperman, author, editor, actor, salesman, and radio announcer. For the past twenty years he has devoted his time to free-lance writing. The author of articles for practically every popular magazine in the country, he has also written a number of books. Among these is THE KIND OF GUY I AM with Robert McAllister. Most of his magazine work in recent years has been for *The Reader's Digest*. THE ELECTRICAL GENIUS OF LIBERTY HALL is his first book for young people.

Mr. Miller makes his home in Nyack, New York, with his wife and son. In connection with his writing, he and the family travel extensively all over the United States.